D1116278

THE FLOWER FAMILY ALBUM

THE FLOWER FAMILY *Album*

FAMILY HISTORIES BY HELEN FIELD FISCHER AND
Radio Garden Consultant

PORTRAITS BY GRETCHEN FISCHER HARSHBARGER
Landscape Architect and Horticultural Illustrator

BONANZA BOOKS • NEW YORK

MANUFACTURED IN THE U.S.A.

Table of Contents

THE FLOWER FAMILY ALBUM

We Wrote This Book for You

Did you know that the Pigweed and the Cockscomb are brothers? The Purslane and the Rose Moss? The Potato and the Petunia?

It's an old story to the botanists, but to those who know their flowers not as specimens but as pleasant companions, there is a big thrill in learning more of their family trees. All too often the scientific language that tells about them seems too difficult for beginners to understand.

This book is a short cut by a pleasant road. We think it will soon have you figuring out flower family resemblances as easily as you can guess to which neighbor belong the children who pass your door.

There are not many flower families represented in our gardens. It is rather a disgrace not to know them when you consider that they feed us, clothe us, and provide our shelter. In fact, any one of several plant families could take care of the world alone, if need be, as you will discover in this book.

We have brought together, family by family, the weeds, flowers, and vegetables that you know best. We could not show them all of course, so we selected a representative sampling. With each group we have given you a key flower that shows strongly the "family look," and have added a few clues that are helpful in making snap identifications.

Each page is like a family reunion in that it contains the plodding and the gifted, the useful and the mischievous, the thrifty and the shiftless, and perhaps even one who has "made good in the city." We have added a little gossip about them to awaken your interest.

The illustrations are all drawn to the same scale. Where individual blossoms are enlarged, they are in scale with each other and about half their actual size. Since individual plants vary because of local conditions, these may not be exactly the height of the ones you know. Where the plant was too bushy to be used full width, we selected typical individual branches. Every picture was sketched from a real, growing plant.

The families are arranged in botanical sequence according to Bailey's *Standard Cyclopedia of Horticulture*. In the spelling of names of flowers we have followed Bailey's *Manual of Cultivated Plants* for cultivated flowers and Gray's *New Manual of Botany* for wild flowers.

We wish to express our gratitude to the ancient writers who wove glamorous legends around flowers; to the soldiers who carried home bulbs and seeds from far countries; to merry-hearted Carolus Linnaeus, who added system to romance; to Asa Gray, who collected and listed our American flora; and to L. H. Bailey, E. L. D. Seymour, Schuyler Matthews, Alfred Hottes, Anna B. Comstock, Donald C. Peattie, and others, who illumined this knowledge and placed it in volumes easily accessible.

In particular we want to thank the thousands of radio friends who have led us on by their eager questions and who furnished living specimens of plants not otherwise available. We are also indebted to Dr. W. A. Anderson, Dr. Clyde Fisher, and E. L. D. Seymour, all of whom gave us valued criticism.

H. F. F. and G. F. H.

How Flowers Developed and Got Their Names

Millions of years ago, when the earth was all under water, there were no flowers! Of course there were plants, but they reproduced themselves by division of cells or other simple methods. And even today two thirds of the plants of the world still get along without flowers.

As the waters began to recede, brave plants crept out into the soggy, foul-smelling new world. They worked out a fine new scheme of reproduction, that of flowers resulting in seeds. Color, fragrance, and varied shapes were developed to attract insects, for in order to produce sturdy seeds the plants needed to exchange pollen with the best of their race. Rooted to the soil themselves, the plants succeeded in persuading the bees and butterflies to do the work for them, by rewarding them with nectar. Since the largest and showiest blossoms got first attention, there was constant improvement.

Then came the matter of distribution. Water was no longer handy for dependable travel, so the mother plants packed lunches in their seed boxes and devised countless ways to hook them onto migrating animals, to float them on the air, or to persuade human beings to carry them from garden to garden.

All over the earth the flowers roamed, meeting people of many languages. Since a flower without a name is as unthinkable as a baby or a kitten without one, there was a grand mix-up, for each plant had many names in many languages.

Botanists came to the rescue. They decided that flowers could be classified by families and named, like humans, to show which children belonged to what parent. Each plant could have any number of local nicknames, but only one standard one. This was written in Latin, the universal language of scholars, so that it would be understood in any part of the world.

What fun as well as responsibility it must be to invent a suitable official name for a newly discovered plant. Many of our familiar flowers were named long ago by early botanists, who knew a surprising lot about the flora of far countries. Ships that sailed distant seas were proud to bring back collections from faraway lands.

Plants have been named for botanists (*Zinnia* was named for J. G. Zinn); explorers (*Lewisia* and *Clarkia* were named for the leaders of the expedition that discovered the part of the country where they are native); legendary characters (*Helenium* was named for Helen of Troy); geographic locations (Gas-Plant, *Dictamnus,* refers to Mount Dicte in Crete); for the place they like to grow (*Nemophila* means "shade-loving"). You can see that there is a story to be hunted out behind each name.

We write the parent, or genus, name first, with the first letter capitalized. Then comes the given, or species, name, which usually begins with a small letter. A variety name may be added to describe some interesting variation in the species. Thus Double Tiger Lily becomes *Lilium tigrinum floropleno.*

These flower children, with their parents, aunts, uncles, and cousins, are known as families. You will find their group portraits in this *Flower Family Album.*

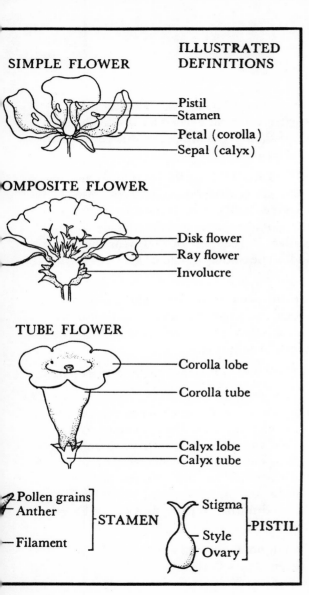

SIMPLE FLOWER

ILLUSTRATED DEFINITIONS

- Pistil
- Stamen
- Petal (corolla)
- Sepal (calyx)

COMPOSITE FLOWER

- Disk flower
- Ray flower
- Involucre

TUBE FLOWER

- Corolla lobe
- Corolla tube
- Calyx lobe
- Calyx tube

- Pollen grains
- Anther
- Filament
STAMEN

- Stigma
- Style
- Ovary
PISTIL

How to Use This Book

If you have the name of a flower and wish to see its picture, you may locate it through the index in the back of the book.

If you have the flower and are hunting for its name, find its general type in the broadly grouped key flowers below. Turn to the pages indicated and study the more detailed key flowers and the clues placed in the upper right-hand corners of the plates.

Or, think of some familiar flower that it resembles, either in its bloom or in its habits of growth. Find the well-known flower through the index, and quite likely your new one will be pictured on a nearby page.

All plants illustrated, discussed, and listed are indexed. Some plants not found in the text are indexed to indicate their relationship.

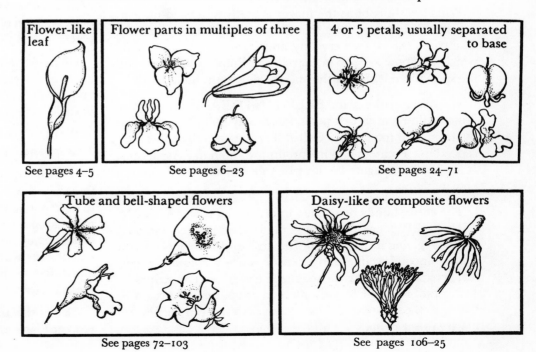

Flower-like leaf
See pages 4–5

Flower parts in multiples of three
See pages 6–23

4 or 5 petals, usually separated to base
See pages 24–71

Tube and bell-shaped flowers
See pages 72–103

Daisy-like or composite flowers
See pages 106–25

3

The Arum or Calla Family

Members of the Calla Family were among the earliest plants in the world. Their young shoots poking through the ground look so much like rearing snake heads that we suspect them of being a device to prevent their being eaten by prehistoric monsters!

Several plants in this family have offensive odors, suggestive of the swampy early world, and they all grow best with moisture, heat, and rich food.

What we think of as the flower is really a dressed-up leaf, developed to protect the true flowers and lure the insects. The true flowers are very tiny and crowded on the thumb, which we know as Jack in Jack-in-the-Pulpit. (Botanists call the specialized leaf a spathe and the flower thumb a spadix.)

We think of the giant ELEPHANTS EAR as a plant to grow behind our garden pools, but nearly half the world cultivates it as a food crop! Called Taro, its starchy tubers are cooked like Potatoes and its sprouts are eaten like Asparagus. It has been propagated so long by tubers that it has forgotten how to bloom.

The entire family has some sort of a fleshy root. JACK-IN-THE-PULPIT has a tuber that the Indians roasted and used for food, giving it the name of Indian Turnip. Uncooked, it is a most uncomfortable thing to taste, since it contains chemical crystals that prick the tongue like needles. The stripes on Jack's pulpit might be well-marked roads for the insects to follow to the honey well. The seeds are showy red berries. Do not try to eat them.

Another native of our moist woods is the GREEN DRAGON. His long nose extends far out beyond his hood. Though wild, he is easily tamed, and you will enjoy his cut-leafed umbrella among your ferns.

The fancy-leafed CALADIUM has foliage more beautiful than its flowers and in an endless variety of colors, usually combinations of red, green, and white. It makes a good window plant or will be a bright spot in a moist, shaded corner of your summer garden. During part of each year the bulb must be dried off and, while resting, should be kept in a warm place.

CALLAS require the same treatment. The white ones grow like weeds along the irrigation ditches in California and Egypt. Some of the yellow ones have transparent places in their leaves that look like silver spots.

WILD CALLA, small and white, is a native of northern swamps and bogs.

Several tropical plants and vines belonging to this family find their way into our indoor gardens. They genuinely prefer to be kept out of sunlight and in warmth, so they are wonderfully adapted to life in our overheated houses and apartments. They do appreciate rich soil and moisture, and some will live in water alone. In this group, none of which are illustrated, we find Philodendron, Nephthytis, Chinese Evergreen, Pothos, and Monstera.

Also of this family but not illustrated are *Acorus Calamus* (Sweet Flag) and *Arum* (Black Calla).

4

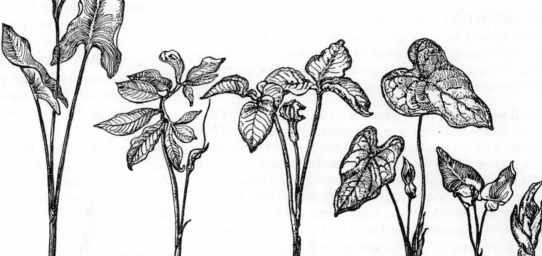

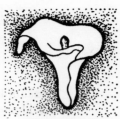

ARUM FAMILY
Araceae
(a-ray'-see-ee)
Leaf wrap-around
Club-like flowers

CALLA
Zantedeschia
(zan-te-des'-ki-ah)

JACK-IN-THE-PULPIT
Arisaema triphyllum
(ar-i-see'-mah)

WILD CALLA
Calla palustris
(kal'-la)

ELEPHANTS EAR
Colocasia esculenta
(kol-oh-kay'-shi-ah)

GREEN DRAGON
Arisaema Dracontium

CALADIUM
Caladium
(kah-lay'-di-um)

SKUNK CABBAGE
Symplocarpus foetidus
(sim-plo-kar'-pus)

5

Spiderworts and Orchids

This family appreciates moisture, though it is fully equipped to get along without it. We know it best by the house plant WANDERING JEW, which is almost as content to grow in a glass of water as in a pot of earth. It is always ready to start new roots from its food-swollen joints. The family bears its flowers in odd leaf cradles in which the buds cuddle like sleeping babies.

SPIDERWORT, a widespread native plant, closes its fragile blue flowers by noon, dissolving them into a drop of thin jelly, which accounts for one of its common names, Widow's-Tear. There are white and pink varieties. The spreading roots may become a nuisance in the garden.

Shall we call the little blue DAY-FLOWER wild? Once started, it scrambles all over the place, and one would lose patience with its weediness were it not for the cheery smile of its monkey faces in shady places. Its scientific name is really a practical joke. There were once three Dutch botanists, the brothers Commelin. Two were conspicuous for their diligence and the third was lazy. When the merry-hearted Linnaeus was naming the Day-Flower, he noted the two showy petals and the third inconspicuous one, and undoubtedly chuckled to himself as he named it *Commelina!*

A decorative tender foliage plant is *Rhoeo* (not illustrated). Its popular names, Moses-in-the-bulrushes and Two-men-in-a-boat, give you a good idea of the way the little flowers are carried. The green and purple leaves form a rosette, with the cradles, or boats, hidden among them at the base.

Some Orchids have taken their feet so far out of the water that they live in trees in tropical jungles! Our native pink and yellow LADY'S SLIPPERS keep their feet on the ground, but their beauty is just as exquisite and fantastic as that of their tropical relatives. You will enjoy figuring out the three sepals and three petals. We will start you by telling that the bulging slipper is one of the petals. All this prankish architecture seems to be just a device to make the insect curious enough to enter, for often no honey is furnished.

The SHOWY LADY'S SLIPPER is the state flower of Minnesota, and a stern law prohibits you from carrying away its pink beauty. It also wears self-protection in the form of tiny glandular hairs poisonous to the human skin.

If you walk in moist meadows during September, you may catch a fragrance similar to that of the Lily-of-the-Valley. You will need sharp eyes to find its source—a short spike of tiny white flowers climbing spirally around a central stem. This is LADIES' TRESSES.

The small pink Orchid of the bogs is named for the nymph ARETHUSA with whom the river god fell in love as she bathed. Its scent is like that of the Violets.

The lavender SHOWY ORCHIS is more easily naturalized than most Orchids. We know this family only as ornamentals, but two of its tropical varieties produce vanilla.

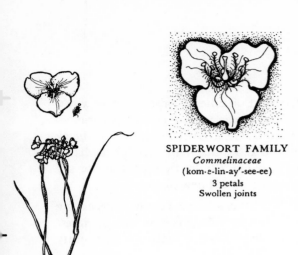

SPIDERWORT FAMILY
Commelinaceae
(kom-e-lin-ay'-see-ee)
3 petals
Swollen joints

ORCHID FAMILY
Orchidaceae
(aur-kid-day'-see-ee)
Irregular flowers
One pouch-like petal

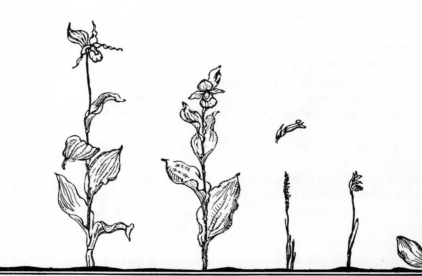

DAY-FLOWER
Commelina
(kom-e-ly'-nah)

SHOWY LADY'S SLIPPER
Cypripedium reginae

ARETHUSA
Arethusa bulbosa
(Ar-ee-theu'-sah)

SPIDERWORT
Tradescantia
(trad-es-kan'-ti-ah)

WANDERING JEW
Zebrina pendula
(ze-bry'-nah)

YELLOW LADY'S SLIPPER
Cypripedium pubescens
(sip-ri-pee'-di-um)

LADIES' TRESSES
Spiranthes
(spy-ran'-theez)

SHOWY ORCHIS
Orchis spectabilis
(aur'-kis)

What Is a Lily?

Many of the flowers that we flatteringly call some kind of a lily do not actually belong in the Lily Family. And, confusingly, many genuine members of the Lily Family do not bear its name! The Onion is of the Lily Family, while the Calla Lily is related to the Skunk Cabbage!

All of the flowers illustrated on the opposite page are true members of the Lily Family. Those on the left are of the genus *Lilium*. You may call them Lily with a firm voice. On the right are the genus *Hemerocallis* and the genus *Hosta*, known as the Day-Lilies and the Plantain-Lilies, respectively. We have shown them all together for comparison.

Blossoms in the Lily Family have six petal-like parts. When you look closely you will find that the three outer ones show a tinge of green or brown on their backs, indicating that they are really transformed sepals. The ovary is carried out of sight within the blossom. The leaves are parallel-veined.

Lilies (the genus *Lilium*) have bulbs made up of loosely overlapping scales. Their stems are clothed in leaves, which upon maturing fill the bulb scales plumply full of plant food to produce blooms the next year. If these scales are removed from the main bulb and planted in sand, they will proceed to use their stored food to develop baby bulbs. So remember to cut your blossoms with a short stem.

The most conspicuous difference between the Lilies, and the Day-Lilies and Plantain-Lilies, lies in the foliage arrangement. The leaves of the latter two do not climb the stem but spring directly from the ground. The stalks that bear the flowers are almost naked. Underground are thick, fleshy roots instead of a scaly bulb.

We chose this assortment of Lilies in order to show you a wide range of flower form and a variety of foliage arrangement. The old-fashioned TIGER LILY, orange with black spots, is typical of all the Lilies that curl their petals backward. The distinctive little black bulbs that grow in the axil of each leaf will tumble out to start new plants.

Our native TURK'S-CAP is another Lily with recurving petals and warm colors, but its foliage is in whorls. In moist places it grows to eight feet. Another native with slightly flaring bells is the CANADA LILY.

The sweetly fragrant ROYAL LILY, or Regal Lily, represents the familiar white trumpet group. They are very hardy and easy to raise from seed.

The dwarf scarlet CORAL LILY is one of the first Lilies to bloom. Its botanical name was formerly *Lilium tenuifolium*. The ELEGANS LILIES hold their yellow or orange chalices open to the sky in clusters of equal height.

The name DAY-LILY is derived from the plant's habit of opening flowers that last for only one day. Fortunately there is always a large supply of developing buds.

The TAWNY DAY-LILY, or Corn-Lily, has become naturalized. The new LEMON DAY-LILIES, developed by crossing various *Hemerocallis*, come in all shades of yellow and orange and bloom at different periods all through the summer. They are very dependable, hardy garden flowers.

PLANTAIN-LILY, often incorrectly called *Funkia*, likes cool shade and moist, fertile soil. The flower colors range from white to lavender.

LILY FAMILY
Liliaceae
(li-li-ay'-see-ee)
Flower parts in 3's
Seed pod inside

TIGER LILY
Lilium tigrinum

CANADA LILY
Lilium canadense

CORAL LILY
Lilium pumilum

TAWNY DAY-LILY
Hemerocallis fulva

WHITE PLANTAIN-LILY
Hosta plantaginea
(hoh'-stah)

TURK'S-CAP LILY
Lilium superbum

ROYAL LILY
Lilium regale

Lilium elegans
(lil'-i-um)

LEMON DAY-LILY
Hemerocallis flava
(hem-er-oh-kal'-is)

**LANCELEAF
PLANTAIN-LILY**
Hosta lancifolia

9

Mostly Spring-Flowering Bulbs

TORCH-LILY, which blooms in late summer, used to be called *Tritoma*. It is popularly called Poker-Plant because of its flaming color. Coming from Africa, it is not hardy in extremely cold winters, so its thick roots are usually dug up and stored in a box of earth. You can easily grow it from divisions of the roots, or if you like to experiment with seed you can have blooming plants the second year.

BOWSTRING HEMP, a tender plant, is known by a variety of names, such as Snake Plant and Mother-in-law's Tongue. Since it will endure heat, drouth, and lack of sun, it is an easy plant to raise in the house. It may be easily started from four-inch cuttings of the leaves inserted firmly in moist sand.

The rest of this page is filled with some of the most common spring-flowering bulbs. Plant them in the fall. CROWN IMPERIAL begins to push its thick head through the soil while the last snows linger and it often needs protection from killing frosts even after it stands two feet tall. It is well worth the trouble, however, for its circle of orange bells hanging under their green crown call forth much admiration. Inside the bell a glistening drop of honey rests at the base of each petal.

Legends say that it once held its bloom proudly erect, but that on the day when Christ passed to His crucifixion it would not bow in sorrow as did all the other flowers. For this it was accursed and shunned until in shame it hung its head and has ever after shed tears of remorse. A less poetic reason for shunning this plant is that both the bloom and the bulb have a very offensive odor.

TULIPS are the high spot of our spring gardens. They like plenty of water both in the fall for root-making and in the early summer, when they are storing food for next year's blooming. Do not cut the leaves until they become limp. Cut the seed pods, however, because seed-making takes strength from the bulbs.

The little CHECKERED-LILY, Snakes-Head, or Guinea-hen Flower, with mottled purple or maroon flowers, will be at home in a rock garden or in light woodland.

STAR-OF-BETHLEHEM, which spreads profusely in old gardens, has white blooms that are touched with green on the outside of the petals.

The fragrant LILIES-OF-THE-VALLEY are easily grown but do not bloom well unless they are uncrowded and have fertile soil. They rarely develop their large red seed balls, which is lucky, for the seeds are poisonous. The strongest pips, dug in late winter, may be flowered indoors.

HYACINTHS are easy bulbs for winter blooming. All you need to do is pot the bulb and keep it in a dark, cool place, well supplied with water, until the blooming shoot begins to push up. Later you can plant it in the garden.

SQUILLS, with their deep blue stars, will grow into large clumps if you see that their seeds are tucked in close by.

The GRAPE HYACINTH is so named because its bloom resembles a cluster of small blue or white grapes.

TORCH-LILY
Kniphofia
(nip-hoh'-fi-ah)

CROWN IMPERIAL
Fritillaria imperialis
(frit-i-lay'-ri-ah)

CHECKERED-LILY
Fritillaria meleagris

LILY-OF-THE-VALLEY
Convallaria
(kon-va-lay'-ri-a)

SQUILL
Scilla
(sil'-ah)

BOWSTRING HEMP
Sansevieria
(san-se-vi-ee'-ri-ah)

TULIP
Tulipa
(teu'-lip-ah)

STAR-OF-BETHLEHEM
Ornithogalum umbellatum
(aur-ni-thog'-ah-lum)

HYACINTH
Hyacinthus
(hy-ah-sin'-thus)

GRAPE HYACINTH
Muscari
(mus-kay'-ry)

Wild Cousins of the Lilies

You'll find most of these flowers growing in the woods. ASPARAGUS, one of the best food producers of the Lily Family, has escaped from old gardens. For more than two thousand years its juicy sprouts have been used for food. Its leaves are the scales that we notice on the young shoots. They soon harden into bracts from which spring the spiney foliage called cladodes. Cladodes do not wilt easily, so all forms of Asparagus make good greens for decorating.

The SOLOMON'S SEALS are so confusing that we have shown them together for comparison. All are alike in having fleshy, creeping roots, and seals, which are the round, sunken scars on the roots where each stem was attached before it died in the fall. The blooms of the true SOLOMON'S SEAL dangle from the leaf axils, while those of the FALSE SPIKE-NARD are carried in a branched, fluffy spray at the tip of its stem. FALSE SOLOMON'S SEAL, a smaller plant than the others, also bears its flowers at the top of the stalk, but they are few and their stems do not branch. You'll like them all in your wild garden.

YUCCAS love hot sunshine. In nature they are at home on steep clay hills and barren rocky wastelands. In our gardens they are especially useful for winter accent material, since their stiff foliage is evergreen. In hot July comes a showy tower of creamy bells. After flowering the plant dies, but fortunately young plants always develop around the old central crown. These carry on, in turn blooming and adding more plants to the clump.

The roots of some species of Yucca furnish a substance used as soap. Unfortunately they also contain a chemical which ruins the quality of milk given by cows that happen to eat its leaves.

To make their seeds Yuccas must have the help of one particular moth, the *Pronuba yuccasella*. Since the larvae of the Pronuba can eat nothing but young Yucca seeds, the female moth lays its eggs in the flower's pistil and then pushes a ball of pollen in after them to make certain that the seeds will develop.

WAKE ROBINS of many kinds, sometimes known as Trillium, are native to our woods. Their three-petaled flowers come in white or in shades of purple. Their fleshy roots stand upright and prefer acid soil, cool shade, and plenty of moisture. When the foliage dies down in midsummer, the plant becomes dormant and may be easily moved to wherever you want it.

The young plant of the yellow BELLWORT somewhat resembles that of the False Solomon's Seal but may be distinguished by the way its stem seems to pierce the base of the leaf. The foliage is handsome all summer and provides pleasing contrast in a shady fern bed.

TROUT LILIES have leaves mottled like the skin of that fish. Perhaps you call them Dog's-tooth Violets because of the shape of the closed flower, or Adder's-tongue. In different parts of the country the colors will vary. They grow from a bulb.

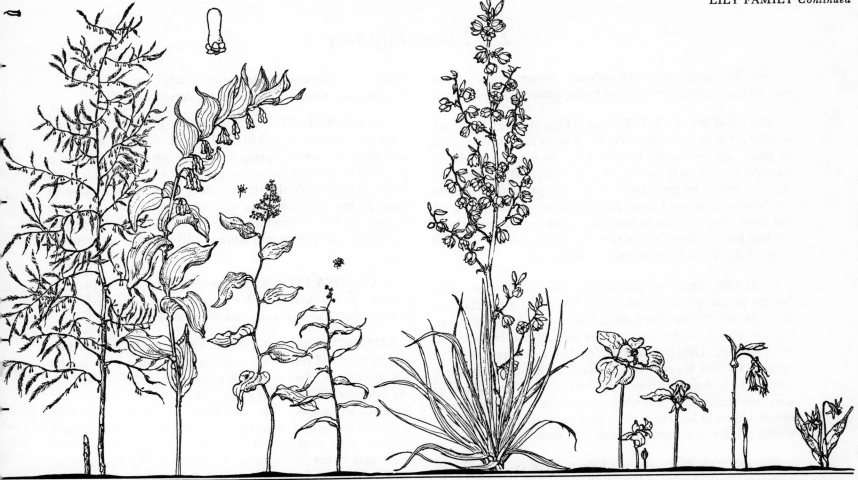

SOLOMON'S SEAL
Polygonatum
(pol-i-gon'-ah-tum)

FALSE SOLOMON'S SEAL
Smilacina stellata

WAKE ROBIN
Trillium
(tril'-i-um)

TROUT LILY
Erythronium
(er-i-throh'-ni-um)

ASPARAGUS
Asparagus
(as-pay'-ra-gus)

FALSE SPIKENARD
Smilacina racemosa
(smy-lah-sy'-nah)

YUCCA
Yucca filamentosa
(yuk'-ah)

BELLWORT
Uvularia
(eu-veu-lay'-ri-ah)

Less Known Lily Folk

Here are some out-of-the-ordinary flowers, mostly bulbous, all hardy, and many native to the western United States.

The DESERT-CANDLE, Foxtail Lily, or Giant Asphodel, sometimes grows to eight feet! Its flowers are white, yellow, or pink, and are closely clustered on the stem. It is winter-hardy if the crown is covered to keep it dry. Like Crown Imperial it starts to grow so early in the spring that it often needs protection from frost. Plants may be grown from seed, but since they are slow in reaching blooming size, most people buy mature roots. When they are once established do not move them, as the large roots are very brittle.

CAMASS, which we use for its spikes of blue or white flowers in our gardens, has a long history as a producer of food. In the Pacific Northwest, where it is a native plant, Camass root was the most valued food of the Indians and early settlers. Tribal wars were fought to gain possession of meadows where it grew, and the Indians did not appreciate having the white men enter with their plows. The bulbs were sometimes eaten raw but were considered better after being slowly baked in hot ashes. You may grow them in your perennial border or naturalize them in a moist, sunny spot.

The ONION illustrated is a wild form of the well-known genus, easily recognized by the hollow leaves, either round or flat, the pink, white, or yellow flowers in umbels, and the odor. Its relatives, such as Chives, Garlic, and Shallots, are used in all parts of the world to flavor food. Egyptian history tells us that the workers on the pyramids once went on strike because they were not furnished Onions in their diet!

CALIFORNIA HYACINTH and BLUE DICKS slightly resemble Onions but lack their flavor. They are wild flowers in California, where spring is a wet season and summer is completely dry. Adapting themselves to the climate, these bulbs rest through the dry months. We can succeed with them in our gardens if we can duplicate western weather conditions. Where summer rains are usual, the bulbs can be lifted after flowering and stored until planting time in the fall.

MARIPOSA LILIES, or Butterfly-Tulips, in gay patterns of white, yellow, and lavender, come from the western United States. They too need a dry rest after flowering.

AUTUMN CROCUS (which is not a true Crocus) is an oddity that will bloom when the proper time arrives in the fall, regardless of whether it is in soil. Place the dry bulb on the window sill or in an empty vase. Day after day fresh blossoms will appear. The bulb must then be set in the garden, and in earliest spring it will put out lusty foliage and produce puffy seed pods. The foliage ripens in June, and the bulbs may either be dug up for house use or be left to become garden subjects.

Also of this family but not illustrated are *Agapanthus* (Lily-of-the-Nile), *Galtonia* (Summer Hyacinth), and *Chionodoxa* (Glory-of-the-Snow).

DESERT-CANDLE
Eremurus
(er-e-meu'-rus)

CAMASS
Camassia
(kah-mas'-i-ah)

ONION
Allium
(al'-i-um)

CALIFORNIA HYACINTH
Brodiaea bridgesi
(broh-di-ee'-ah)

BLUE DICKS
Brodiaea capitata

MARIPOSA LILY
Calochortus
(kal-oh-kohr'-tus)

AUTUMN CROCUS
Colchicum
(kol'-ki-kum)

The Amaryllis Family

The flowers of the Amaryllis Family look very much like those of the Lily Family. The most obvious difference is the position of the ovary. In Lilies it is enclosed and smoothly hidden by the six petal-like parts. In Amaryllis it is a conspicuous bulge extending below these showy parts. Watch for that telltale bulge!

The leaves of the two families are also similar, both having long parallel veins. The leaves of Amaryllis tend to be strap-shaped and blunt-tipped. Amaryllis bulbs are solid rather than scaly.

TUBEROSE is native to Mexico and needs a long hot season to mature its bloom. It may be started indoors and later set barely under the ground in full sun. The bulb that blooms will die, but it will be surrounded by many smaller ones, each of which will bloom when larger. Dig up the bulbs after the first frost and store them in a warm, dry cellar.

HARDY AMARYLLIS, or Surprise-Lily, is truly hardy. Promptly in the spring the leaves appear, gather food, and then wither. In August comes the surprise. Within the short space of three or four days the bloom stalk will spring nakedly from the soil, grow to thirty inches, and open its lily-like clusters of iridescent, lavender-pink flowers. A dozen stalks make a picture worth going miles to see. They may be moved after blooming.

HOUSE AMARYLLIS requires careful ripening of its leaves after blooming and then a dry period of rest. They bloom best when crowded in the pot, and the bulbs should be set only one third under the soil. Plants grown from seed will flower in three years if given no rest period. After that they should be handled as old bulbs.

The LILYBASKET, Ismene or Peruvian Daffodil, is a tender bulb that produces its spider-legged white blooms in early summer and then matures its leaves. It should be stored in a warm cellar for the winter. Leave the roots on the bulb.

The fragrant Narcissi, in shades of yellow or white, have cup-like centers of various lengths. The long-trumpet kinds are commonly called DAFFODIL. The small, cluster-flowered, yellow ones are the true Jonquils, though some people use this name for the large-trumpet types. All of the genus like some shade. All are hardy except the tazettas, such as the Paper-Whites, Soleil d'Or, and Chinese Sacred-Lily.

ZEPHYR-LILY is a dwarf plant with dainty flowers of pink or white to grace our summer gardens. Because it sends up new buds after each rain it is often called Rain Lily. You may also know it as Fairy-Lily. It must be dug in the fall to escape frost but may be used as a house plant.

The tiniest member of this family is the wild GOLD EYE GRASS, which blooms with Violets in the spring. You will find it on the prairie.

Even earlier comes the SNOWDROP, which likes a moist, sunny location in the spring and a shady one in summer.

Also of this family but not illustrated are *Agave* (Century Plant), *Crinum, Nerine* (Guernsey-Lily), *Eucharis* (Amazon-Lily), *Leucojum* (Snowflake), and *Sprekelia* (Jacobean-Lily or St.-James-Lily).

3'

2'

1'

6"

AMARYLLIS FAMILY
Amaryllidaceae
(am-ah-ril-i-day'-see-ee)
Flower parts in 3's
Seed pod outside

HARDY AMARYLLIS
Lycoris squamigera
(ly-koh'-ris)

LILYBASKET
Hymenocallis calathina
(hy-men-oh-kal'-is)

ZEPHYR-LILY
Zephyranthes
(zef-i-ran'-theez)

SNOWDROP
Galanthus
(gah-lan'-thus)

TUBEROSE
Polianthes
(pol-i-an'-theez)

HOUSE AMARYLLIS
Hippeastrum equestre
(hip-ee-as'-trum)

DAFFODIL
Narcissus
(nahr-sis'-us)

GOLD EYE GRASS
Hypoxis hirsuta
(hy-pok'-sis)

The "Poor Man's Orchid"

The Iris Family is another family whose flowers have six showy parts. Three of the parts are often inclined to be larger than the others. A more constant identifying characteristic is the way in which the leaves are carried, one astride the next higher one. The Latin word for this is equitant, meaning "like a horseback rider." You will find the ovary beneath the flower, as in the Amaryllis Family.

The name Iris means "rainbow," which is an apt description of the range of colors in this family. Though history refers to Iris as "the lilies of France" and our grandmothers called them Flag Lilies, they are not Lilies!

The Iris is such a popular garden flower that we are all familiar with its shape. But where are the stamens and pistil? We've made a drawing to show them to you and to explain the clever hidden device that insures cross-pollination.

The pistil divides into three, long, strap-like stigmas, under which are hidden their own pollen-covered anthers, which the stigmas strive to avoid. On the throat of each lower petal (fall) is a velvet "beard," or "rug," leading to the honey at its base. The bee, his back covered with pollen from the last flower visited, lights on this rug and pushes his way under the stigma strap. The stigma takes as much pollen as it wants and then springs up to avoid any of its own pollen, with which the bee will be newly laden as he backs out. That's why Iris never come true from seed and why they have almost endless color combinations.

The GERMAN IRIS, with its conspicuous beard and fleshy rhizome, is the one with which we are most familiar. It will grow almost any place but prefers sunshine and well-drained soil. Transplanting should be done soon after the flowering season. At that time the old roots are shed and new ones develop which will anchor the rhizome in readiness for winter. The SIBERIANS bloom a little later and are more slender in build. They too are easy to grow. The white form is lovely for Memorial Day use.

The JAPANESE IRIS loves the waterside and has large blooms in July, when the main Iris show is past. They are spectacular in size and shape.

VESPER IRIS flowers in August, opening each afternoon about two o'clock with many small blooms like lavender butterflies. Imagine the combination when it is grouped with the pink Hardy Amaryllis, which blooms at the same time.

BLUE FLAG and COPPER IRIS are native plants, the former from the Midwest being a delicate blue, and the latter from Louisiana being a copper-red color. Both appreciate moisture.

ROOF IRIS is a dwarf type often grown in the thatched roofs of the Orient. Our native tiny CRESTED IRIS comes in the same colors of lavender and white. Its slender, creeping rhizomes form a thick mat among hospitable rocks or in a wild garden.

Rapidly growing in popularity are the DWARF IRIS. Absolutely hardy, they open their blossoms in April, along with the earliest Tulips. They can be had in a wide range of colors, white, yellow, pale blue, purple, and dozens of bee-mixed combinations.

IRIS FAMILY
Iridaceae
(i-ri-day'-see-ee)
Flower parts in 3's
Overlapping leaves

GERMAN IRIS
Iris germanica
(i'-ris)

SIBERIAN IRIS
Iris sibirica

JAPANESE IRIS
Iris Kaempferi

BLUE FLAG
Iris versicolor

VESPER IRIS
Iris dichotoma

COPPER IRIS
Iris fulva

SPANISH IRIS
Iris Xiphium

ROOF IRIS
Iris tectorum

DWARF IRIS
Iris pumila

CRESTED IRIS
Iris cristata

Iris Relatives

We know that these are members of the Iris Family because of their six-parted flowers, the equitant leaves, and the ovary beneath the flower.

The GLADIOLUS is one of our most popular tender bulbous flowers. The bulbs must be dug, carefully labeled, and stored during the winter in a warm, dry place. Some varieties multiply so very much faster than others that the rare ones are soon outnumbered and often lost. This sometimes causes people to think that the choice ones changed color, but it has been proved that bulbs always exactly repeat the parent bulb, except that poor cultivation or hot sun may make the color slightly paler. All changes must be made through seed.

The BLACKBERRY LILY is so called from the resemblance that its seed head bears to that fruit—in looks only! These seeds are used for winter bouquets, and a cluster of them is quite striking in a white vase. This plant selfsows so freely that it is almost a weed in old gardens, but it is receiving new recognition as a border subject because it blooms in August, when perennials are scarce.

AFRICAN IRIS is a treasured house plant from the Orient. Its bud stalk springs from the edge of its leaf and produces fairy Iris blooms in white, yellow, and blue. Each bloom lasts only a day, but the same stalk furnishes new ones daily for weeks. After the bud stalk ceases to bloom, it may be removed and rooted. Perhaps you call this the Twelve Disciples Plant.

The FREESIA is valued especially for its rare fruity fragrance, though its flowers in white, lavender, or yellow are graceful and beautiful. It is a common garden flower in California, where it blooms in February and March. The bulbs are inexpensive and may be easily brought into bloom for house plants if they are kept cool enough. They should be potted in early September and kept in the light. When freezing weather approaches, bring them into a cool, sunny room, the temperature of which should be about forty-five degrees. Keep the soil barely moist. The plants will not get leggy unless the room is too warm. When the buds are ready to open, plants may be brought into the living room. After blooming, keep them watered until the leaves ripen, and then the bulbs may be used year after year. Freesias bloom the second year from seed.

Are you surprised that the little BLUE-EYED GRASS is an Iris? It is easy to understand if you examine it closely. It is native to American prairies, where it dots the grass with blue or white on sunny mornings. In the afternoon the blossoms are closed. Transplant it to your garden, but mark it well, so that you will not weed it out along with escaped lawn grass.

The CROCUS blooms in earliest spring. In Holland, where they grow wild, the yellow ones are called Meadow Saffron and their dried anthers are often used for coloring food, especially boiled rice. You will enjoy trying some of the species that bloom in the fall.

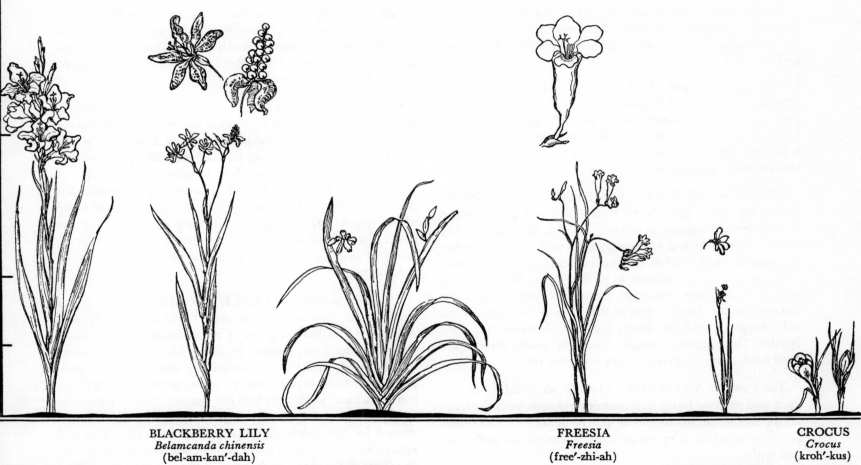

GLADIOLUS
Gladiolus
(glad-i-oh'-lus)

BLACKBERRY LILY
Belamcanda chinensis
(bel-am-kan'-dah)

AFRICAN IRIS
Marica
(ma'-ri-kah)

FREESIA
Freesia
(free'-zhi-ah)

BLUE-EYED GRASS
Sisyrinchium
(sis-i-rin'-ki-um)

CROCUS
Crocus
(kroh'-kus)

21

Two Notorious Weeds, and the Loosestrifes

The Mulberry and Nettle families have little to offer our gardens, and we have included them only because they contain two infamous and highly publicized weeds. Behold them and beware!

Who hasn't heard of Marijuana, which furnishes the dreadful drug sometimes known as hashish? You will find it growing innocently along fence rows and highways, where it is known as the weed HEMP. The seeds are beloved by both wild and tame birds, and it produces a useful fiber. Ramie cloth is made from an Asiatic Hemp.

STINGING NETTLE! The family name *Urticaceae* means "to burn," and the sting they give is due as much to their chemical content as to their needles. In ancient times doctors lashed the skin of their patients with Nettle branches to cause counterirritation, the process being called urtication.

If you are foolish enough to go into moist lowlands with your arms and legs unprotected, you will find a convenient remedy for the Nettle's itch in the juice of the plant of the wild Snapweed, which usually grows in the same area with Nettles. Unappetizing though it sounds, young Nettles are sometimes eaten for greens. They are good, too.

The fern-like ARTILLERY PLANT, so useful for terrariums and window boxes, is a harmless relative from the tropics. It likes moist, loamy soil. It gets its name from the explosive way in which it opens its buds, throwing the pollen far and wide.

The flowers of the Loosestrife Family sometimes have no petals! When there are petals, they are set casually into the top rim of a long calyx tube instead of down inside, as in most flowers. Sometimes this calyx tube takes on varied colors, as in the tender CIGAR-FLOWER, which has a red calyx edged with yellow.

Cuphea FIREFLY is a new and exciting arrival in our annual gardens. Some call it patriotic because its floral scheme is red, white, and blue. Around the top of its calyx tube is a band of white into which are daintily set ruffled petals of red, while the loyal stamens complete the scheme with plumes of blue-purple. Others call it exotic, rather than patriotic, because the individual blooms are almost exact copies of those of its relative, the Crape-Myrtle (not illustrated) of the South. In spite of its gorgeous headgear the plant lacks refinement because it sprawls its coarse branches untidily on the ground.

The wild perennial PURPLE LOOSESTRIFE makes a rose-colored glow over moist wastelands during July and August. If you have a pond or an informal pool, you may naturalize this plant around the edges. Moisture is not essential, however, and since Loosestrife is one of the few pink perennials that bloom during midsummer, its improved form has been welcomed into our borders. Try it with blue Chinese Larkspur and soft yellow Marguerites, or as a background for the naked-stemmed Hardy Amaryllis. You will appreciate it for bouquets all through late summer. Its petals, like those of *Cuphea,* are inserted at the top of its calyx. You will enjoy splitting one with a pin and examining it.

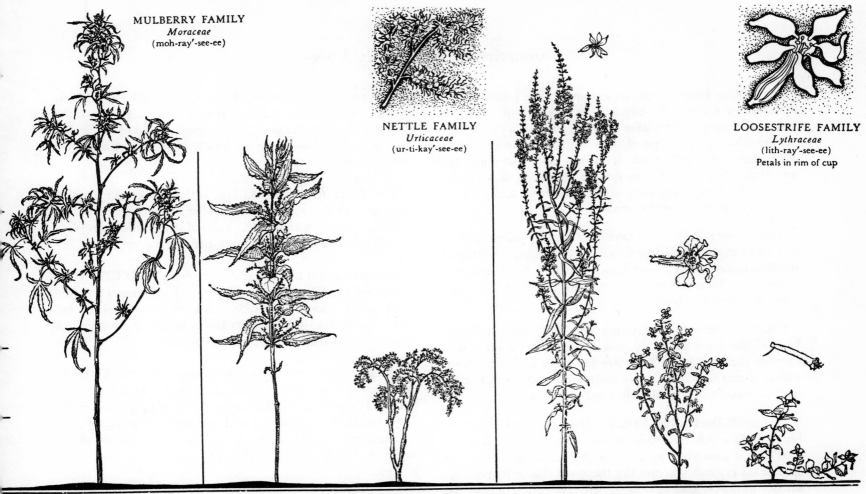

MULBERRY FAMILY
Moraceae
(moh-ray'-see-ee)

NETTLE FAMILY
Urticaceae
(ur-ti-kay'-see-ee)

LOOSESTRIFE FAMILY
Lythraceae
(lith-ray'-see-ee)
Petals in rim of cup

HEMP
Cannabis
(kan'-ah-bis)

STINGING NETTLE
Urtica
(ur'-ti-ca)

ARTILLERY PLANT
Pilea microphylla
(py'-le-ah)

PURPLE LOOSESTRIFE
Lythrum Salicaria
(lith'-rum)

FIREFLY
Cuphea
(keu'-fe-ah)

CIGAR-FLOWER
Cuphea ignea

Smartweeds with Many Knees

The "many knees" are conspicuous swollen joints, usually sheathed in a tissue-like bandage at the base of each leaf. This sheath braces the leaves onto the stem. Another identification clue is the shape of their seeds, three-edged like a Brazil nut. Sometimes there are wings along the edges and sometimes they are flat. The flowers are small, often having sepals only. Frequently they are dull-colored, and they are never conspicuous except in mass.

The family is inclined to have sour, watery juices, and the leaf stalks of the RHUBARB make delicious sauces and pies. Its slightly medicinal properties are welcome, but the mature leaves have been suspected of causing poisoning, so teach children not to eat them.

Greens prepared from young leaves of the CURLED DOCK also have a slightly acid taste and are a great delicacy in the spring. Its seeds are favorites with wild birds, which means that it is widely scattered, to the regret of the farmer, who finds it a difficult weed to destroy.

The small Dock called FIELD SORREL is a fast-spreading pest. It is reported to be poisonous to horses and sheep. Don't let it into your garden, for the thread-like roots will spread faster than you can dig them out. Since its presence usually indicates acid or sour oil, an application of lime will help in the battle. Sheep Sorrel, an *Oxalis,* is no relation.

A few members of this family are used in flower gardens. One of them, a very tall Smartweed with large heart-shaped leaves, bears the romantic name of Kiss-me-over-the-garden-gate! A more dignified name for it is PRINCES PLUME. If grown in very rich, warm soil it will reach high above the garden gate and dangle pink feathers that are six inches long. It is a selfsowing annual. In China the leaves are dried and smoked.

The dwarf SMARTWEEDS, which make the stubble fields pink in late summer, are similar and are a rich source of honey (the dark kind). The juice of some varieties is acrid enough to cause the skin to smart, hence the name.

Another garden favorite is the climbing FLEECE-VINE, or Silver-Lace Vine. Its dangling panicles (clusters) of fragrant white blossoms combine especially well with blue Morning-Glories. It is not fully hardy in severe climates but is easily grown from either seeds or cuttings.

The best food producer of the family is BUCKWHEAT. We think of it merely in connection with breakfast pancakes, but the pioneers used it for a staple food supply when early crops failed, for Buckwheat will mature even when sown in midsummer. It too is a fine honey plant. A mean climbing weed is FALSE BUCKWHEAT. Keep it out of your garden.

The most widespread member of the family is too small to illustrate. It is the gray-leaved Knotgrass, or Dooryard grass, that tries to mantle every bare yard, no matter how well trodden. Examine it and you will find tiny green Smartweed blossoms and green bandages on every knee.

BUCKWHEAT FAMILY
Polygonaceae
(pol-i-goh-nay′-see-ee)
Tiny flowers in sprays
Swollen joints

RHUBARB
Rheum Rhaponticum
(ree′-um)

FLEECE-VINE
Polygonum Auberti
(poh-lig′-oh-num)

CURLED DOCK
Rumex crispus
(roo′-meks)

FALSE BUCKWHEAT
Polygonum scandens

PRINCES PLUME
Polygonum orientale

SMARTWEED
Polygonum Hydropiperoides

BUCKWHEAT
Fagopyrum
(fag-o-py′-rum)

FIELD SORREL
Rumex Acetosella

25

The Everlasting Pigweeds

For a family of very little importance either for its food or for its flowers, and with several disreputable members, this one does a lot of strutting! How it loves color!

Its plants have no petals. The richly colored combs and plumes are made up of stiff sepal scales called bracts. Since these bracts retain their color when dry, the plant was given the name *Amaranthus,* meaning "unfading." The Greeks called it the flower of immortality and used it for funeral purposes. In olden times its seeds were ground into a coarse meal for making Lenten bread, and the leaves of some of the plants are used as greens.

The family tendency toward highly colored foliage develops better in poor soil than in rich, and the seeds of all species refuse to germinate before hot weather, since none are native to cold regions. Any of the plumes will hold their color well if dried, heads down, before the seeds begin to ripen. They are used effectively in some modernistic flower arrangements but must be handled with caution because of their oddity. The giant COCKSCOMBS are grown for curiosities rather than for beauty. Their bracts form great convoluted masses a foot or more across and are the typical Amaranth red.

PRINCES FEATHER, with its softer pink and yellow plumes, has a sort of garden grace in spite of its coarse leaves. There is beauty of line, also, in the long tails of Love-lies-bleeding (not illustrated).

Even the tall, hairy ROUGH PIGWEED attempts plumes, but they are a washed-out green color. You will find various forms of this weed, including a trailing one, which, when dry, rolls into a ball and makes a Tumble Weed. Though Pigweeds are annuals, their seeds seem to live almost forever in the soil. Don't let the plants reach seeding age. Pull them or cut them while young.

There is real beauty in GLOBE AMARANTH with its round, clover-like blossom heads. Its colors range from white through the pinks to deep carmine, and there is one variety in soft orange-bronze. They make good garden subjects when massed in single colors and stand up well as cut flowers for hot weather use. The little heads when dried and placed on individual wires are used in winter bouquets.

The foliage plant called BLOODLEAF is of this group. It has smooth red leaves with pink veins, and once a year bears the telltale Pigweed bracts. Because of the translucency of its leaves it is seen at its best when placed where the sun will shine through them. Besides the red form, there is one with green leaves beautifully patterned in white and red.

JOSEPHS COAT, in both the dwarf and larger size, is another red-leaved foliage plant. It is the great stand-by for bordering flower beds in parks and cemeteries. Its oriental colorings remain beautiful far into the fall. It is very easily rooted from cuttings and is useful in terrarium, dish, or window gardens. Examine the next one you see for the tiny bract flowers that show its origin.

PIGWEED FAMILY
Amaranthaceae
(am-ah-ran-thay′-see-ee)
No petals
Colored scales

COCKSCOMB
Celosia argentea
(se-loh′-shi-ah)

ROUGH PIGWEED
Amaranthus retroflexus

BLOODLEAF
Iresine
(i-re-sy′-nee)

PRINCES FEATHER
Amaranthus hypochondriacus

GLOBE AMARANTH
Gomphrena globosa
(gom-free′-nah)

JOSEPHS COAT
Amaranthus tricolor
(am-ah-ran′-thus)

27

Part-Time Flowers

The two families on this page are alike in their disinclination to keep their flowers open all day. But they don't agree as to time! Some of them open only in full sun, while others prefer the twilight hours.

The Four O'Clock Family name *Nyctaginaceae* means "night-flowering," which describes its habits. We have pictured first the wild form, called UMBRELLAWORT because of the green umbrella involucre, which holds the small, seed-like, true flowers. What seems to be a magenta corolla is really a calyx. This may carry you farther into botany than you care to go just yet, but it is interesting to know that the colored Four O'Clock flowers are not what they seem!

FOUR O'CLOCKS are splendid plants for a quick landscape effect, as they quickly make shrubs of themselves for foundation planting or hedges. It is almost impossible to get true colors from seed, but if you mark the ones you wish to save, they may be dug up in the fall and stored like Dahlia roots.

A spectacular tropical relative that drapes itself over walls and fences in warm climates is Bougainvillea (not illustrated). In the north it is grown in greenhouses. Its bright color also comes from its calyx.

The Purslane Family likes to bloom in sunshine! The leaves and stems of its plants are fleshy. The well-known weed PURSLANE, or Pusley, has a bad reputation, but perhaps it is trying to be nature's farmer. Putting down only one tiny root for anchor, it spreads its succulent leaves over vast spaces, which it keeps cool and moist. Europeans eat it as salad and some Americans find it excellent as greens.

PORTULACA, or Rose Moss, is a very close kin. It has the same fat leaves, open-top seed boxes, and flowers that open only in the sun. Rose Moss too refuses to grow except in hot weather, and it seems to live on air, so small is its root. It is an annual that makes a colorful ground cover for hot, difficult places.

TALINUM is a sort of wild hardy Rose Moss. Its foliage is good in the rock garden, and so are its magenta flowers, except that they stay open little more than an hour in the late afternoon.

The gorgeous pink BITTER-ROOT, the western member of the family, was named for Captain Lewis of the Lewis and Clark expedition. It is the state flower of Montana and gets its common name from the taste of the skin on its fleshy root. It was a source of food for the Indians.

It is said to have been grown in England from a dried herbarium specimen, but it has proved not as easy to grow in the corn belt! Give it a sunny, well-drained spot in your rock garden and you may succeed. All effort will be well repaid.

A Midwest native is the dainty pink SPRING BEAUTY. It may also have been used for food because it grows from a potato-like tuber. We find no such record, however, and would like to know if this is true.

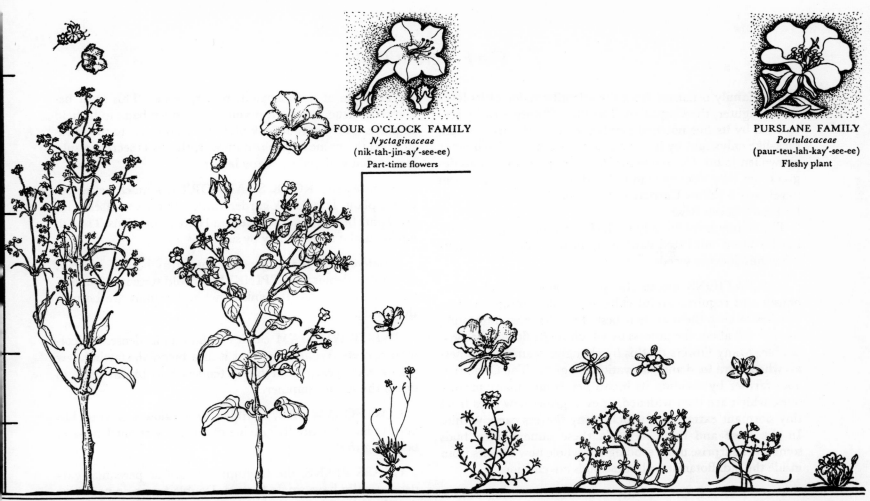

FOUR O'CLOCK FAMILY
Nyctaginaceae
(nik-tah-jin-ay'-see-ee)
Part-time flowers

PURSLANE FAMILY
Portulacaceae
(paur-teu-lah-kay'-see-ee)
Fleshy plant

UMBRELLAWORT
Oxybaphus
(ok-sib'-a-fus)

FOUR O'CLOCK
Mirabilis Jalapa
(my-rab'-i-lis)

TALINUM
Talinum
(tah-ly'-num)

PORTULACA
Portulaca grandiflora
(paur-teu-lay'-kah)

PURSLANE
Portulaca oleracea

SPRING BEAUTY
Claytonia virginica
(klay-toh'-ni-ah)

BITTER-ROOT
Lewisia rediviva
(leu-is'-i-ah)

29

The Fragrant Pinks

This family is named from the scientific name of its loveliest daughter, the Carnation. The Pink Family is easily recognized by its five notched petals spreading flat from a tall, sack-like calyx and by its leaves that are opposite each other at swollen joints. Of course the Pinks are pink, in various degrees, but they also come in red and white. The florists even developed a yellow Carnation, but it proved no more popular than a green Rose.

The family is useful only for its beauty and fragrance and has far more cultivated varieties than wild ones. It contains a few mischievous weeds.

CARNATIONS bloom the year around in cool greenhouses and require careful cultivation and protection from diseases to keep them at their best. They have an interesting story to tell about the process by which single flowers become double. Many flowers do this by changing stamens into petals when extra food and cultivation are given. The Carnation goes farther by dividing its broad petals into many narrow ones, which are then widened. It even grows new ones from tiny dormant extra buds, which many flowers carry within. In the Rose and the Calendula these same hidden buds sometimes surprise us by sending out whole new flowers from inside the old. Botanists call these buds adventitious.

The STARRY CAMPION is a white-flowering native. The genus is called Catchfly because some species carry a sticky gum high on their stems to keep out unwelcome insect visitors. Many are night bloomers.

Old-fashioned BOUNCING BET is the gardener's horrible example of an obnoxious root spreader. This fault becomes a virtue, however, if you have a steep bank to be held in place. The fragrant pink blossoms lend grace to the roadside. As the name *Saponaria* implies, the roots secrete a substance that will make a soapy lather.

Its little sister ROCK SOAPWORT is a much better behaved plant. It is a rock garden trailer that covers itself with vivid pink blossoms in the driest and hottest locations. Though a perennial it spreads only by seeds.

A native plant that is good for the hardy border, rockery, or wild garden, is PEATPINK. In its wild state it is found in sandy or rocky soil. Its pink or white blossoms are born in the spring.

SWEET WILLIAM carries its flowers in dense, varicolored clusters. We usually treat it as a biennial, starting new plants each year, for it has a tendency to bloom itself to death the second summer.

COW SOAPWORT, a brilliant cerise-flowered weed, has been found contentedly gracing many a flower garden—and behaving too!

GRASS PINKS, the fragrant pets of our perennial gardens, usually have single flowers. Double forms do not come true from seed but are best grown from root divisions. You will find many fine, new varieties listed and pictured in your nursery catalogues. Carnation and Grass Pink have been crossed to produce sturdy garden Carnations. These are fine for edging paths or flower beds and in rock walls.

PINK FAMILY
Caryophyllaceae
(kar-i-oh-fi-lay'-see-ee)

5 petals, deep calyx
Swollen joints

STARRY CAMPION
Silene stellata
(sy-lee'-nee)

BOUNCING BET
Saponaria officinalis
(sap-oh-nay'-ri-ah)

CARNATION
Dianthus Caryophyllus

SWEET WILLIAM
Dianthus barbatus
(dy-an'-thus)

COW SOAPWORT
Saponaria Vaccaria

GRASS PINK
Dianthus plumarius

PEATPINK
Silene pennsylvanica

ROCK SOAPWORT
Saponaria ocymoides

31

More Members of the Pink Family

Perennial BABYS-BREATH when blooming is the frothy filler of the perennial border. When dried it is used as the background of nearly all winter bouquets. Because of its long, tough roots it defies drouth but hates transplanting. The double varieties are best, but as they do not come true from seeds, they are usually propagated by grafting. The pink forms are not very satisfactory as yet.

For winter use, harvest just as soon as the flowers are well open and hang them, heads down, in a dry place. Slow drying, or moist storage, causes the flowers to turn yellow, which spoils the charm of its misty whiteness. Leave at least twelve inches of stem on the plant to strengthen the root and supply fall bloom. When handled in winter the dried stalks should first be placed in a moist atmosphere for a few hours to make them pliable.

ROSE CAMPION is sometimes called Mullein-Pink, because its soft, woolly, gray leaves resemble those of the wild Mullein. It is a perennial, with vivid magenta, or rarely white, blooms.

One of the worst weeds in the wheat fields is the CORN COCKLE, introduced to America from Europe. It is very hairy, with calyx spikes that extend beyond the purple petals. Cockle refers to the seeds, which are not as bristly as those of the Cocklebur but have fine barbs that are unwholesome to livestock. The seeds are supposedly poisonous and are therefore a dangerous impurity in wheat.

MALTESE CROSS, known also as Jerusalem Cross and Scarlet Lightning, is of such a fiery scarlet that it must be tactfully separated from other reds in our gardens. It is easy to cultivate, doing almost equally well in sun and shade. If you keep it from seeding, it will bloom again for you in the autumn. Occasionally you will see double forms.

Lychnis Haageana (not illustrated) is a larger flowered, lower growing hybrid, with blossoms two inches across and often in softer shades of red. You will enjoy trying it from seed.

STARRY CERASTIUM, or Mouse-ear Chickweed, is a bad spreader in cool, moist situations. In dry rock gardens, however, it becomes a treasured beauty, making a mound of appreciated white bloom early in the spring.

CREEPING BABYS-BREATH is another good rock garden plant, which is at its best tumbling over the brink of a wall in airy whiteness. Trim it back after flowering. Because it blooms only once, some consider it less useful than its little cousin *Tunica Saxifraga* (not illustrated), called Tunicflower or Coat Flower because it wears its calyx up around its shoulders. It comes in a soft shade of pink and in both single and double varieties. It blooms during August and September as do very few other trailers.

CHICKWEED is famous, but for the doubtful honor of being the most widely distributed weed in the world. Though it is an annual, it blooms and seeds so very early that it gets ahead of the most vigilant gardener.

Also of this family but not illustrated are *Arenaria* (Sandwort) and *Spergula* (Spurry).

BABYS-BREATH
ypsophila paniculata
(jip-sof′-i-lah)

CORN COCKLE
Agrostemma Githago
(ahg-roh-stem′-ah)

STARRY CERASTIUM
Cerastium arvense
(se-ras′-ti-um)

CHICKWEED
Stellaria media
(ste-lay′-ri-ah)

ROSE CAMPION
Lychnis Coronaria

MALTESE CROSS
Lychnis chalcedonica
(lik′-nis)

CREEPING BABYS-BREATH
Gypsophila repens

Buttercups

There are so many interesting members of the Buttercup Family that we are spreading them over four pages. The blooms vary from tiny inconspicuous ones to some of the most elaborate and colorful of the flower world. Surely they have lived down their original, unflattering name, which comes from the words meaning "little frog." But they have never forgotten that their feet love wet soil.

The distinctive family trait is the bunched seed head. This may be a cluster of long pods or a burry ball of hard, hooked, individual seeds (called achenes). You will also find many stamens and divided foliage in great variety. Watch for these clues. On this first page the flowers look as Buttercups should, but on the following pages they don deeper and deeper disguises.

GLOBE-FLOWER is a gorgeous aristocrat for moist, sunny spots in our gardens. The blossoms, in yellow or orange, are carried on tall, smooth stems above deeply cut foliage. They are especially attractive when contrasted with purple Japanese Iris, which likes the same cultural conditions.

There are many native types, such as BULBOUS BUTTERCUP and SWAMP BUTTERCUP, whose glossy yellow cups are a welcome sight in spring meadows but which soon become nuisances under cultivation.

Even the double CREEPING BUTTERCUP is a doubtful blessing, though her sister TALL BUTTERCUP, of which we show a spray, keeps her place and is especially good when planted with Oriental Poppies and the yellow and brown bi-colored Iris. Use it as a filler in your border and for gay bouquets on your breakfast table.

If you have a shallow pool in your garden, plan for an April treat in the form of a mass of golden MARSH-MARIGOLDS, or Cowslips. They have great, waxy leaves, the only uncut ones in the family, and such glowing yellow petals that they never fail to prove that you "love butter" when a bunch of the blooms is held under your chin. They are native along streams and in damp meadows.

You will find PHEASANTS-EYE listed among the annuals in most seed catalogues. It has bright and interesting flowers in red and yellow and might pass for a member of the Daisy Family were it not for its clustered seed heads.

Earliest of all is the CHRISTMAS-ROSE, which is such a bad sleeper that it may awaken and open its white blooms during some warm spell in November instead of waiting for March. Plant it where it can have protection and sunshine in winter and shade in summer.

If it likes the home you provide, it will repay you by gradually increasing its size and the number of its blooms. The petal-like parts are sepals. There are several species of *Helleborus,* some with flowers carrying a purplish tinge.

WINTER ACONITE, its little yellow-headed sister, is almost as impetuous and is best grown in colonies where the sun cannot find her too easily. Like Christmas-Rose, it too has evergreen leaves.

BUTTERCUP FAMILY
Ranunculaceae
(rah-nun-kew-lay'-see-ee)
Clustered seed pod
Cut-leaf foliage

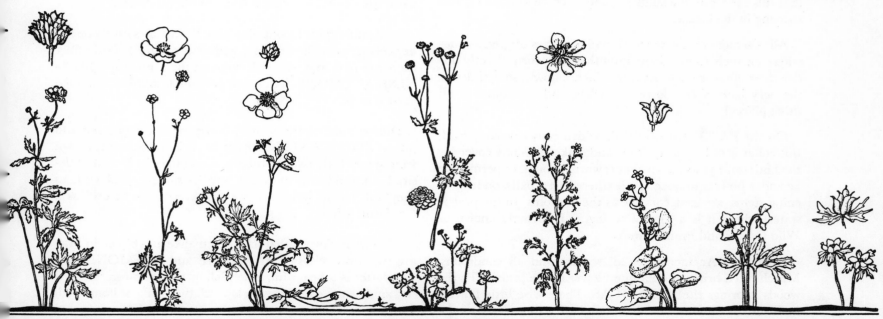

GLOBE-FLOWER
Trollius
(trol'-i-us)

SWAMP BUTTERCUP
Ranunculus septentrionalis
(rah-nun'-keu-lus)

TALL BUTTERCUP
Ranunculus acris

PHEASANTS-EYE
Adonis
(ah-doh'-nis)

CHRISTMAS-ROSE
Helleborus
(hel-ee-bor'-us)

BULBOUS BUTTERCUP
Ranunculus bulbosus

CREEPING BUTTERCUP
Ranunculus repens

MARSH MARIGOLD
Caltha palustris
(kal'-thah)

WINTER ACONITE
Eranthis hyemalis
(e-ran'-this)

Anemones with Collars

This page displays the Anemone group of the Buttercup Family. They show their Buttercup blood plainly by their clustered seed heads, divided leaves, and many stamens.

Anemone is Greek for "windflower," a name that is especially suitable for the wild, white MEADOW ANEMONE that fills the waste lowlands in June, each head nodding and swaying in the breeze.

All Anemones wear flaring circular collars of green somewhere on their stems. Sometimes they are worn directly under their chins, sometimes a few inches down, sometimes at the very base of the flower branches, and sometimes in all three places!

On the PASQUE FLOWER, which comes warmly clad, this collar is of long gray "fur" and makes a woolly cover for the buds until a day comes that is warm enough to permit the lavender flowers to open. Its feathered seed balls, on lengthening stems, are as decorative as the blossoms. In the prairie states, where it is a sign of spring, it is lovingly known as Wild Crocus and Prairie Smoke.

There are Anemones for all seasons and all conditions. March often brings the Pasque Flower to the prairie. To the woods it brings the HEPATICAS. These wise little flowers make use of the sunshine that comes after the trees are bare in the autumn to develop leaves and flower buds for spring. The leaves prepare a woolly covering for themselves and a similar collar for the buds. But while the leaves are still folded in their winter sleep, the buds push out pale pink and lavender faces, drawing back into their warm collars when late snows arrive. Because of the shape of their leaves they are sometimes called Liverwort.

The open prairie in June supplies the THIMBLEWEED, which we seldom notice while in bloom but rather in the fall, when each thimble wears a fleece of "lamb's wool."

September finds blooms like pink Wild Roses on *Anemone hupehensis* (not illustrated), and even as late as November there are pink and white blossoms on the aristocratic JAPANESE ANEMONE. These are perennials and like a shaded garden nook.

During most of the winter, florists offer the gay red and purple POPPY ANEMONE, or St. Brigid Anemone, grown from queer little twisted tubers, which may be forced as desired. In California they are garden subjects and with us they will bloom indoors if we can keep them as cool as a California winter.

Two wood flowers that look much alike and bloom in May are the white WOOD ANEMONE and ANEMONELLA. The latter is a beautiful, pale pink or white flower, which is not an Anemone but a very close relative. Take it home with you, for it is so happy under the conditions of a protected shade garden that it responds with larger flowers and sometimes with extra petals. It increases rapidly, both from self-sown seeds and from divisions of its little tubers. Its lacy foliage remains attractive all summer.

THIMBLEWEED
Anemone virginiana

POPPY ANEMONE
Anemone coronaria

HEPATICA
Hepatica
(he-pat'-i-kah)

WOOD ANEMONE
Anemone quinquefolia

JAPANESE ANEMONE
Anemone japonica
(ah-nem'-oh-ne)

MEADOW ANEMONE
Anemone canadensis

PASQUE FLOWER
Anemone Pulsatilla

ANEMONELLA
Anemonella thalictroides

Buttercups in Deep Disguise

Meadow Rue has leaves so much like those of Columbine that very few people can tell the young plants apart when found together in the woodland. Both have leaves divided in series of threes, but Meadow Rue far outdoes the Columbine in this tendency.

The lovely **COLUMBINE MEADOW RUE** is named *Thalictrum aquilegifolium,* which means "the Thalictrum with foliage like Columbine." They admit it! This one is also called Feathered Columbine because its flowers are a feathery mist of lavender or pink stamens. Imagine its beauty clumped with tall pink Iris which blooms at the same time. It is extremely hardy and should be a "must have" for all perennial borders.

The **TALL MEADOW RUE** is shown in an unusually short specimen here, but it often grows to six and eight feet if given moisture and some shade. Its creamy stamens make picturesque masses that are at their best when placed back of a pool where they will reflect in the water. They invite insects neither by perfume nor by petals but are satisfied with the self-pollination given them by the wind. Perhaps, having seen their mirrored reflection, they feel they have already achieved the ultimate in beauty.

In the **LARKSPURS** the spur is a two-celled honey sac covered with an extension of one of the sepals, wrinkled like "the wrist of a suede glove." How this genus does love to dress up! And it is the sepals that take on the vivid blues and dreamy lavenders and look like petals. But on the back near the tip you will find a green blotch that proves they are using

"petticoats for dresses." It is really an arrangement for supporting the awkward bumblebee while he gets his honey. It is funny to see the air of ecstasy with which he embraces this welcome support while his long tongue goes far into first one cell and then another.

ROCKET LARKSPUR is a most useful annual to get going in a hardy border, for its seedlings bloom at exactly the dull time in early July. Weed out any surplus. Be sure to get the newer strains, for there's a lot of difference.

There are several wild Larkspurs, some of them poisonous to cattle, but cattle never eat them unless driven to it by extreme hunger. We have shown only **PURPLE LARKSPUR.**

Can you think of any use for the hood on **MONKSHOOD**? Of course it protects the stamens, but a stamen's place is out in the open! It would almost seem that it was dressed-up to make us eager to invite it into our gardens, even though its roots, and sometimes its flowers, are poisonous. The drug aconite comes from the European *Aconitum Napellus* (not illustrated).

COLUMBINE makes all of its petals into honey spurs, and its sepals into rainbow-colored wings, then sets the flowers dancing on slender stems. It is a perennial.

There was nothing left for **LOVE-IN-A-MIST** to do in the way of a novel arrangement of her flower, so she joined her seed pods into an odd puffy ball to amuse us, and her blue eyes peer roguishly out from a mist of green. Another name for this plant is Gretchen-in-a-bush! It is an annual.

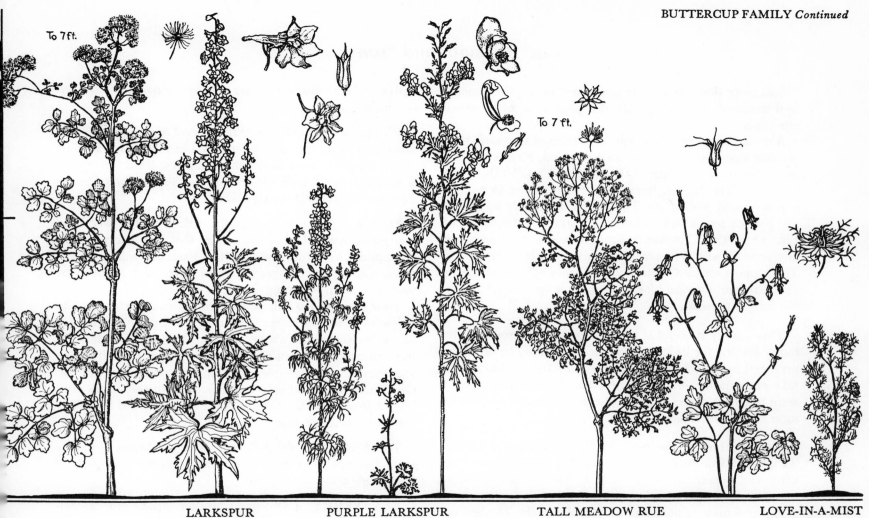

To 7ft.

To 7 ft.

LARKSPUR
Delphinium
(del-fin′-i-um)

PURPLE LARKSPUR
Delphinium bicolor

TALL MEADOW RUE
Thalictrum polygamum

LOVE-IN-A-MIST
Nigella damascena
(ny-jel′-ah)

COLUMBINE MEADOW RUE
Thalictrum aquilegifolium
(tha-lik′-trum)

ROCKET LARKSPUR
Delphinium Ajacis

MONKSHOOD
Aconitum
(ak′-oh-nyt-um)

COLUMBINE
Aquilegia
(ak-wi-lee′-ji-ah)

39

Clematis and Peony

Still more Buttercups! Are you remembering the bunched seed heads of this family? On this page some of them will grow tails!

Although there are hundreds of varieties of Clematis, there are two that always come quickly to mind. First with all of us is the fragrant white AUTUMN CLEMATIS, which blooms in late August. Because its flowers hang in panicles it was named *paniculata*. The blooms are made up of four waxy-white sepals and a cluster of stamens (a family clue). Like every other Clematis it climbs by hooking its leaves over any support within its reach and giving their stems a twist. The support for all Clematis vines should be rigid, for if the vines are bent or wind-blown, the bark is apt to split and admit fungus growths.

This variety is useful if left trailing on the ground in the hardy border, for its long sprays of bloom may be lifted and arranged to cover bare spots as needed. After a frost its leaves take on metallic tints and its feathered seed head makes it seem to bloom again. It is the hardiest Clematis and has the most abundant foliage.

Next we think of the great purple JACKMAN CLEMATIS, which is a little harder to establish but when once satisfied will persist for generations. It likes an east exposure, excellent drainage, a little lime, and a heavy application of rotted cow manure once a year. Water it freely. The best one we ever saw was under a leaky eaves spout!

The SCARLET CLEMATIS is a pretty species that is native to Texas and sometimes goes by the name of *Clematis coccinea*.

We are showing only one of the several bush types—*Clematis integrifolia*. This one is very good in the border, sending out its purple blooms all summer long. A splendid white one is *Clematis recta* (not illustrated), while *Clematis Davidiana* (not illustrated) is pale blue.

Even though you look carefully at the PEONY seed head and leaves it will be hard to realize that it is a sister to the Larkspur. The wild Peonies of the mountains would show it more plainly, for the garden types have been changed by years of careful breeding.

Your greatest joy will be had from giving perfect care to a few ultrafine varieties. Give them well-drained soil in a sunny location, and, above all else, plant them shallow. If the crown is more than two inches deep after the soil settles, you may never have a bloom. Use no fertilizer at the root. Give them abundant water and do not cut the leaves until after a frost. The best time to move them is in the fall. They are ideal cemetery plants.

The FRINGED PEONY with fine-cut leaves is a very early bloomer. The flowers are dark crimson and come in both single and double forms.

BANEBERRY, a woodland brother, upsets our calculations by having berries! But he still has quantities of stamens and cut leaves. There are both red and white fruiting forms, but the flowers are always white.

AUTUMN CLEMATIS
Clematis paniculata

JACKMAN CLEMATIS
Clematis Jackmani

PEONY
Paeonia albiflora
(pee-oh'-ni-ah)

FRINGED PEONY
Paeonia tenuifolia

SCARLET CLEMATIS
Clematis texensis

Clematis integrifolia
(klem'-ah-tis)

WHITE BANEBERRY
Actaea alba
(ak-tee'-ah)

41

The Poppies

The common name of this family might well come from the manner in which the green sepals pop off when the flower opens.

The Poppy Family offers little food to the world. As if beauty were its own excuse for being, it proudly displays its gorgeous silken petals and sculptured leaves.

From its juices comes poppy-seed oil, used as a substitute for olive oil and as a dryer in paint. And the narcotic opium is made from the milky gum of the Opium Poppy, *Papaver somniferum* (not illustrated). Only its juice is narcotic. We eat the seeds freely on pastry and they are fed to canaries as a tonic under the name of maw. The annual double-flowered Poppy is a development of the Opium Poppy.

Many of the species bear their seeds in a pepperbox, which shakes the seeds out a few at a time. Others have long slender capsules similar to those of the Mustard Family.

The family prefers cool weather but has thick milky juices to resist evaporation. Like all other milky-juiced plants, Poppies will keep fresh in water only when the ends of the stems have been seared in heat.

PLUME POPPY, the showy-leaved giant of the family, has no petals. The white or pink plumes are masses of stamens. Use it for background, but be forewarned that it is a bad spreader.

ORIENTAL POPPY was originally a gaudy scarlet but has been developed into subdued maroons, pinks, and lavenders. To reproduce choice plants one must make root cuttings during the August dormant season. Transplanting is also done at this time.

SHIRLEY POPPIES were developed at the vicarage in Shirley, England, only about fifty years ago. Among the common red Poppies of this type, which are weeds in Europe, the vicar discovered one with white edges. He isolated it and from its progeny developed the pink, white, and variegated darlings that are the "grace notes" of our June gardens. They are annuals. Sow the seed where you wish the flowers, for they are difficult to transplant.

The stem of ICELAND POPPY springs unbranched and without leaves from a rosette of evergreen foliage, thus earning its scientific name *nudicaule*. It blooms the first year from seed and in cool, well-drained soil will furnish flowers in a gay assortment of colors all summer.

The yellow flowers of CELANDINE, clustered among evergreen leaves, bloom the year around in sun or shade. Its bright orange juice is useful for removing warts. It is a perennial.

The roots of BLOODROOT are quite bloody with a red juice, which, when dropped on a lump of sugar, was an old-fashioned cough remedy. It is one of our earliest and most exquisite wild flowers. Each blossom bud pokes through the soil with a leaf shawl around its shoulders. This leaf rapidly enlarges after flowering and remains picturesque all summer.

Many members of the Poppy Family are natives of the West, such as the annual golden CALIFORNIA POPPY and the bristly PRICKLY POPPY with flowers of white, yellow, or lavender. Two not illustrated are Cream-Cups and Matilija Poppy.

To ten ft.

POPPY FAMILY
Papaveraceae
(pah-pay-ver-ay'-see-ee)
4 petals, showy juice
Deep-cut leaves

PLUME POPPY
Bocconia
(bok-oh'-ni-ah)

PRICKLY POPPY
Argemone
(ahr-je-moh'-nee)

ORIENTAL POPPY
Papaver orientale
(pah-pay'-ver)

SHIRLEY POPPY
Papaver Rhoeas

ICELAND POPPY
Papaver nudicaule

CELANDINE
Chelidonium majus
(kel-i-doh'-ni-um)

BLOODROOT
Sanguinaria
(san-gwi-nay'-ri-ah)

CALIFORNIA POPPY
Eschscholzia
(esh-shol'-zi-ah)

43

This family, called *Fumariaceae* from the nitrous fumes given out when it is pulled, is easily identified since it always wears it heart on its sleeve, swaying gracefully in plain sight. The foliage is lacy and the juice watery.

BLEEDING-HEART, with its rows of dangling valentines, is sometimes referred to as an old-fashioned flower but was introduced from China only a hundred years ago. The lobes of the heart are produced by two large petals that stretch restraining arms around the stamens, which arch sidewise and outward in their efforts to escape. Meanwhile the other two petals, very narrow ones, reach upward to cover both the tip of the pistil and the anthers. Only the bees know what it is all about. Someone has said, "Flowers don't care what we think about them. It is the insects' opinion that matters!"

Bleeding-Hearts do well in semishade and are especially lovely behind masses of Forget-me-nots. They ripen their leaves and become dormant after blooming. Try them as a winter house plant, after allowing them a taste of outside freezing weather. If you wish to try your hand at propagation, they come easily from root cuttings.

The FRINGED BLEEDING-HEART is one of the few perennials that bloom freely all summer. While its hearts are paler and narrower than the usual type, their persistent foliage makes them attractive at all times. They like rich, moist soil and will grow in shade. The seed must lie in the ground during the winter to germinate.

CLIMBING FUMITORY, or Allegheny Vine, is the daintiest of climbers. It likes a moist, shady place out of the wind. It is a biennial that selfsows when once established. The first year it makes only a crown of leaves, but the second year it will climb twenty feet and produce hundreds of little pink hearts.

The wild yellow CORYDALIS has blooms that are not exactly hearts, but neither do they resemble any other flowers, and its leaves plainly proclaim their ancestry. It is a weedy plant, low-growing in the shade but taller when it creeps into the garden. Farther north there is a wild form with rosy-purple flowers.

DUTCHMAN'S BREECHES and SQUIRREL CORN are two similar charming natives. The difference is more easily explained by the pictures than by any words. In the Dutchman's Breeches the flower lobes flare sharply with an angular effect, while the Squirrel Corn has rounded lobes with a pinker tinge and is more fragrant. Their root systems show differences also. When you dig them up, one will have tubers clinging together to form one large bulb. The other will be a mass of little bulblets, scattered and shaped like little grains of corn. Can you guess which is Squirrel Corn? Both will be very happy in your wild garden, but like their big sister, the Bleeding-Heart, they will disappear almost like magic once they are through blooming, to appear again each spring. Although they both like moist, rich woodlands, they are seldom found growing together.

44

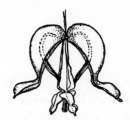

BLEEDING-HEART FAMILY
Fumariaceae
(feu-may-ri-ay'-see-ee)
Heart-shaped flowers
Ferny foliage

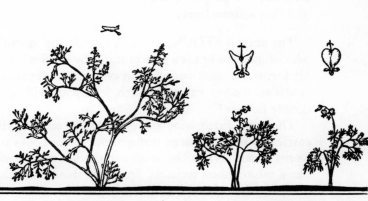

CLIMBING FUMITORY
Adlumia
(ad-leum'-i-ah)

CORYDALIS
Corydalis aurea
(koh-rid'-al-is)

SQUIRREL CORN
Dicentra canadensis

BLEEDING-HEART
Dicentra spectabilis
(dy-sen'-trah)

FRINGED BLEEDING-HEART
Dicentra eximia

DUTCHMAN'S BREECHES
Dicentra Cucullaria

45

The Peppery Mustards

This family is named *Cruciferae,* meaning "cross bearers," because of its four-petaled flowers. It furnishes most of our supply of hot-tasting vegetables. Some, like Water Cress, are eaten for their leaves, and some, like Radish, for their roots. Even the weed forms are so wholesome that sailors eat them to prevent scurvy, and call them Scurvy-Grass. However, since these weeds reproduce freely, they are a troublesome lot for farmers.

The showiest garden flower of the family is DAME'S ROCKET. Its flowers are crude, but by mass production, fragrance, and willingness to bloom in the shade, it has won an enviable status. Their colors, ranging from white through lavenders to purple, combine well with Iris. Though biennial they selfsow freely.

The annual STOCK, in the same coloring, doesn't like the heat of gardens but is a winter stand-by for florists. The double forms are most popular but only the single ones set seed. A skilled worker can tell which seed pods will produce the double flowers!

The most fascinating pods are found on HONESTY. It carries its seeds in large transparent pocketbooks for all the world to see. When the seeds are shed, a center membrane like a white moon remains. Sprays of these moons are treasured for winter bouquets. It is a biennial.

SHEPHERD'S PURSE is the most widely scattered weed in the world, with the exception of Chickweed. It is named from the shape of its seed pod and may be destroyed by spraying it with iron or copper sulphate. Peppergrass (not illustrated), which the birds especially enjoy, is in the same class.

The WALLFLOWER comes in vivid oranges and yellows, and if planted in the fall will burst into bloom by Tulip time in the spring. They take their name from a liking for the crevices in limestone walls.

GOLDEN-TUFT, or Basket-of-Gold, wins its name *saxatile* from the Latin for "rock breaker." It is a mass of yellow flowers at Tulip time. After blooming, trim it back severely to strengthen it for the next year. Sow seeds where you want them to remain, for mature plants cannot be easily moved.

ROCK-CRESS is usually the earliest perennial to bloom, which endears it to us even though its white flowers are simple. *Aubrietia* (not illustrated) is similar and comes in shades of lavender but, alas, never lives long in hot climates.

In annuals we have the useful CANDYTUFT, so called because it is a native to Candia (Crete). It comes in shades of purple and pink and blooms five weeks after planting. When the first crop fades, plant more for the cool days of fall. There is a perennial, evergreen, white Candytuft (not illustrated).

Last but most indispensable is the annual SWEET ALYSSUM, which gives the finishing touch of white lace to our flower beds and borders. Though not everblooming it is easily made to seem so by clipping half of each plant alternately so that fresh growth is always coming on.

MUSTARD FAMILY
Cruciferae
(kroo-siff'-er-ee)
4 petals
Peppery taste

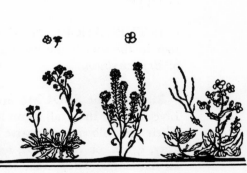

AME'S ROCKET
esperis matronalis
(hes'-per-is)

STOCK
Mathiola incana
(mat-hy'-oh-lah)

HONESTY
Lunaria annua
(leu-nay'-ri-ah)

SHEPHERD'S PURSE
Capsella
(kap-sel'-ah)

WALLFLOWER
Cheiranthus
(ky-ran'-thus)

CANDYTUFT
Iberis
(y-bee'-ris)

GOLDEN-TUFT
Alyssum saxatile
(ah-lis'-um)

SWEET ALYSSUM
Alyssum maritimum

ROCK-CRESS
Arabis
(ar'-ah-bis)

47

Succulents

Because of its thick fleshy leaves the Orpine Family is well prepared for hot, dry seasons, when it will have to live upon stored moisture and food. Dried herbarium specimens have been known to start growing off their pages!

The sure way to kill one of them is to give it too much water, for then it will drink until it bursts its tender cells. If grown in pots without drainage, hold the water to a teaspoonful a day. If they need more, they will indicate it by sending out little aerial rootlets.

Visitors to Florida often bring back leaves of the AIR-PLANT. When pinned to a curtain in a sunny window, the leaf will soon produce a row of little plants around its edge. These may be allowed to grow an inch or more long before being potted.

In TUBE AIR-PLANT the tiny plants drop off and catch root in the soil. Some botanists call this *Kalanchoë* instead of *Bryophyllum*.

Many of the SEDUMS are hardy, and under the name Live-for-ever their tall forms have been used for generations. Their pink blooms are coarse but colorful, and their foliage, gray, green, or variegated, retains its waxy beauty through all hardships. They make ideal plants for the dry, narrow strip often found between the sidewalk and the house.

JADE-PLANT, a tender house plant with thick green leaves and slow growth, has an oriental effect, for it looks as if it were made of that precious stone. Water it sparingly and keep its leaves dusted. Old plants give profuse crops of simple but fragrant white flowers.

To learn the difference between the tender and the hardy Hen-and-Chickens you will have to study the pictures carefully. The ECHEVERIAS are all natives of Mexico and cannot stand freezing. Their smooth leaves are in pale shades of green.

HOUSELEEKS are darker green, winter-hardy, and inclined to be hairy. Because they are grown in the roofs of thatched cottages, their common name becomes obvious. Another name arising from this source is Welcome-home-husband-though-ever-so-drunk!

They must have excellent drainage and protection from hottest sun. When the central rosette reaches full maturity it sends up a thick, leafy bloom stalk, ripens its seeds, and dies. Its many offspring eagerly fill the vacant space. Seeds grow easily, producing many new varieties, to the delight of collectors.

KALANCHOE, with its vividly red clusters of flowers, is a recent addition to the florist's pot plants. It is hard to get into bloom early enough for Christmas, but Valentine's Day also calls for red. For the summer set it directly in the ground in semishade. Repot in the fall and put in a sunny window.

GOLD MOSS with yellow flowers is a typical trailing *Sedum*. There are hundreds of others, with many variations of leaf and color. They are especially useful for pockets in our sunny rock gardens, enduring heat, drouth, and storms. Some forms are much more weedy than others.

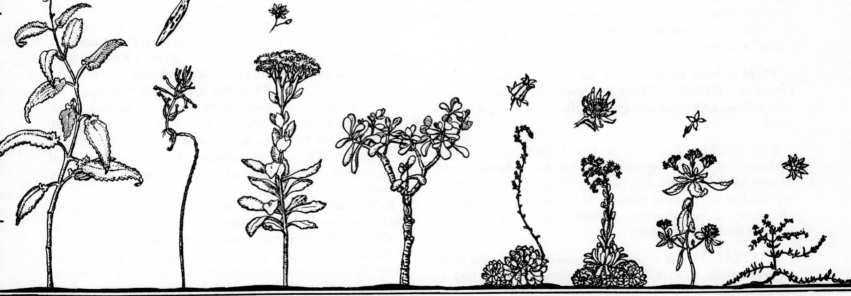

ORPINE FAMILY
Crassulaceae
(kras-eu-lay'-see-ee)
Fleshy leaves
Long-lasting flowers

TUBE AIR-PLANT
Bryophyllum tubiflorum

JADE-PLANT
Crassula arborescens
(kras'-eu-lah)

HOUSELEEK
Sempervivum
(sem-per-vy'-vum)

GOLD MOSS
Sedum acre

AIR-PLANT
Bryophyllum crenatum
(bry-oh-fi'-lum)

SHOWY SEDUM
Sedum spectabile
(see'-dum)

ECHEVERIA
Echeveria
(ek-e-vee'-ri-ah)

KALANCHOË
Kalanchoë coccinea
(kal-an-koh'-ee)

49

The Rose Family

The Rose Family has flowers with five petals, and their stamens are in a ring around the edge of a sunken cup. Among its fruit members (not illustrated) are Apple, Quince, Plum, Peach, and Strawberries, Raspberries, and Blackberries. Its best-known shrub is Spiraea.

The weed relatives, such as the burry AGRIMONY and the yellow-flowered meadow CINQUEFOIL, do not look very rose-like, but if you are willing to hunt, you will find the distinctive circle of stamens. Cinquefoil means "five-fingered" and refers to its leaves.

There is little in the family for our perennial gardens. Geum or CHILOE AVENS has jewel-like colorings of red and yellow, and some low-growing forms of Cinquefoil are good.

STRAWBERRY does a fine job of changing the family perfume into one of the most delicious flavors in the world. It now has an everbearing, never-trailing variety that is being used to edge flower borders. It has good foliage and an abundance of long, slender, red berries, which make it popular with birds and children.

DALIBARDA is a creeping perennial native with white strawberry-like flowers. It will adapt itself to your rock or wild garden.

Now about ROSES! Every part of the world has some sort of a wild Rose. They differ in many ways but are alike in having five-petaled single blossoms and the ability to come true from seed. These are called Species Roses, and are used for rootstock on which to graft more delicate varieties. As they would quickly outgrow and smother these guests if allowed to develop sprouts of their own, grafted plants must be watched closely, so that wild suckers from the rootstock may be removed.

What we call tame Roses have been developed slowly. Double blossoms were secured by persuading stamens to turn into extra petals. Desired traits of color, foliage, and hardiness came mostly from crossbreeding or accidental sports.

So complicated has the crossbreeding been that it is almost impossible to trace any of our choice garden Roses to their wild parentage. They are called horticultural varieties, and the most useful ones fall into the following five groups.

Hybrid Perpetuals have strong, hardy wood, large blossoms on old wood in June, and scattering bloom in the fall.

Hybrid Teas have tender wood that dies to the ground every winter. Through the summer there is a succession of large flowers on new wood. They are best when used as cut flowers.

Baby Ramblers differ from the Hybrid Teas in having smaller flowers in large clusters. They are best for bedding.

The very hardy Rugosas make large bushes and are used as shrubbery planting for hot, dry locations. Their heavy foliage is always attractive, as are their continuous blossoms and bright seed hips. Other good shrub roses are the fragrant Sweetbriar, early yellow Hugonis, and Redleaf Rose.

Climbers do not really climb, but have long, limber, up-reaching shoots that may be fastened to trellises. Some bloom on old wood, others on new. Don't prune your plants until you have studied their flowering habits.

3'

2'

ROSE FAMILY
Rosaceae
(roh-zay'-see-ee)
5 petals
Stamens in circle

AGRIMONY
Agrimonia
(a-gri-moh'-ni-ah)

ROSE
Rosa
(roh'-zah)

CINQUEFOIL
Potentilla
(poh-ten-til'-ah)

AVENS
Geum canadense
(jee'-um)

CHILOË AVENS
Geum chiloense

STRAWBERRY
Fragaria
(fray-gay'-ri-ah)

DALIBARDA
Dalibarda repens
(dal-i-bahr'-dah)

The "Rock Breakers"

Saxifragaceae means "rock breaker," so you won't be surprised to discover that most of this family will make themselves at home in your rock garden. Their leaves are as decorative as their flowers.

They differ bewilderingly but usually bear numerous blossoms on a slender stem sent up from a rosette of leaves. The color range is from white through pink, and rarely yellow. Shrubby kin are the Gooseberry, Currant, Mock-Orange, and Hydrangea.

ASTILBE is often incorrectly called Spiraea, which it resembles. (Spiraea is a shrub belonging to the Rose Family.) It has attractive cut leaves and plumes of white or pink flowers. If you should be given one as an Easter pot plant, be sure to set it in your garden later, for it is a hardy perennial. Give it rich soil and moisture in either sun or shade.

Some of the family have such tiny petals that only the calyx cup is conspicuous, resembling a bell. This is the case with *Heuchera*. The wild ones, called ALUM ROOT, vary in appearance and soil preference in different parts of the country. Those native to the prairie like sunshine, while those of eastern mountains are adapted to shade and moisture. In general they have attractive large leaves and scapes of pale green bell-shaped flowers.

The garden type, CORAL BELLS, may range from pale pink to deepest coral and is a treasure for a moist, shady location, especially appreciating acid soil. The seeds do not come true, so it is best to propagate by root divisions or crown cuttings.

Another good garden flower is the LEATHER SAXIFRAGE. The scientific name *Saxifraga crassifolia* means "a rock plant with very coarse leaves," but these leaves are glossy and beautiful, and the spikes of rosy flowers are a pronounced addition to the April rock garden.

VIRGINIA SAXIFRAGE is a native found on dry, rocky hillsides in April, with white flowers followed by brilliantly purple, two-beaked seed vessels.

FOAM-FLOWER spreads its cooling leaves over the forest floor all summer and carries feathery sprays of white flowers in May or June. They are made conspicuous by the orange tips on their ten stamens. The seed pod, shaped like a tiara, gives it the name of *Tiarella*.

BISHOPS-CAP, or Miterwort, resembles the Foam-Flower, but its flowers, shaped like snow crystals, are fewer in number and carried closer to the stem. Two little leaves, opposite one another, form a collar just under the flower spike. The seed pod is the miter.

The so-called Strawberry-Geranium (not illustrated) is not a Geranium at all, but *Saxifraga sarmentosa!* A familiar house plant with silvery leaves and fluffy flowers, its popular name comes from its habit of sending baby plants out on long runners. Another of its well deserved names is Mother-of-Thousands.

SAXIFRAGE FAMILY
Saxifragaceae
(sak-si-frah-gay'-see-ee)
Leaves in basal rosette
Naked flower stem

ALUM ROOT
Heuchera Richardsonii
(heu'-ker-ah)

LEATHER SAXIFRAGE
Saxifraga crassifolia
(sak-sif'-rah-gah)

FOAM-FLOWER
Tiarella
(ty-ah-rel'-ah)

ASTILBE
Astilbe japonica
(a-stil'-be)

CORAL BELLS
Heuchera sanguinea

VIRGINIA SAXIFRAGE
Saxifraga virginiensis

BISHOPS-CAP
Mitella diphylla
(mi-tel'-ah)

53

The Peas

This is one of the families that is prepared to take care of the world alone, if need be. It is fortunate for us that it is friendly, for it is one of the largest families, having more than seven thousand species, including trees, vines, and herbs.

The family name *Leguminosae* means "pod." True pods open along two sutures, and we find most members of this family storing their seed in such containers. We eat them.

Of course you know what the typical Pea blossom looks like. Rarely its five petals group themselves like the blossom of a Rose (as in *Cassia,* page 56), but in most of the family they look more like butterflies. One petal enlarges to make a banner to tell the bees that pollen is ready. Two more, called wings, make a roof landing field for the bees. The last two join to make a cradle for the ovary, which is wrapped in a gossamer sheet made from the united stems of the stamens.

In some members of the Pea Family self-pollination is the rule. The leaves are divided and many have a tendency to close at night or even when touched in the daytime.

Of great horticultural importance is the fact that Legumes, in partnership with certain soil bacteria, collect nitrogen from the air and transform it into compounds that plants can use for food. The bacteria workshops are the nodules which you will find on the roots of Legumes. Farmers plant Alfalfa, Clovers, and other Legumes to build up depleted soil.

Among tall natives useful in perennial borders are THERMOPSIS and WILD INDIGO. Thermopsis prefers moist soil and is the less branching. Its spikes of yellow bloom fairly glow in the border and are good when massed with pale blue Larkspur. WILD INDIGO likes dry prairie conditions and has white, yellow, and purple forms. It sleeps late in the spring, but once up, grows rapidly. The foliage is attractive throughout the summer, and the striking dark seed pods are distinctive as winter bouquet material.

Garden forms of perennial LUPINE seem very difficult for Americans to grow. Ours have done best when in poor soil, partly coal ashes. Inoculation of the seeds with nitrogen-fixing bacteria usually helps. Colors vary from white through yellow, pink, and lavender.

TICKCLOVER is a woodland and prairie native that gets its name from the habit of dividing its very hairy pod into triangular sections, which stick to the passer-by like ticks. In this way its progeny get out into the world.

The BLUEBONNETS of Texas are annual Lupines, which grow by the acre down there but do not thrive in northern gardens. I wish someone knew why.

The dread LOCOWEEDS of the plains cause the death of thousands of cattle and sheep yearly. We illustrate one of the most deadly ones. It has white blooms and when the pods are dry the seeds inside make a "rattlebox."

The PEANUT pushes its yellow flowers under ground in order to ripen its pods.

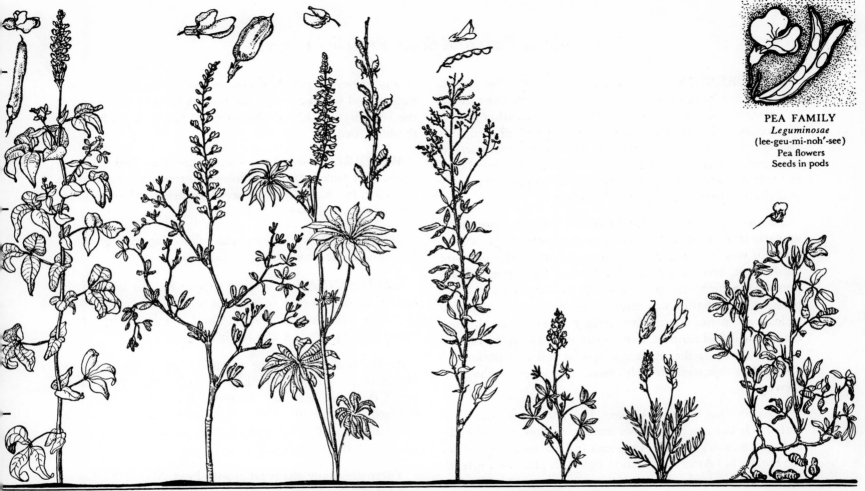

PEA FAMILY
Leguminosae
(lee-geu-mi-noh'-see)
Pea flowers
Seeds in pods

THERMOPSIS
Thermopsis caroliniana
(ther-mop'-sis)

WILD INDIGO
Baptisia
(bap-tiz'-i-ah)

LUPINE
Lupinus polyphyllus
(leu-py'-nus)

TICKCLOVER
Desmodium
(des-moh'-di-um)

BLUEBONNET
Lupinus texensis

LOCOWEED
Oxytropis Lamberti
(ok-sit'-roh-pis)

PEANUT
Arachis hypogaea
(ar'-ah-kis)

55

Climbing Peas and Some Prairie Flowers

The PERENNIAL PEA is not fragrant like the annual kind, nor are its blooms as large. But it is much more useful in semiarid regions because drouth and hot weather do not discourage it. Even during August days a porch draped with clusters of its flowers will seem, at a distance, to be covered with pink or white Roses. It makes an excellent ground cover for banks and terraces. Like many other Peas it climbs by tendrils that permit it to give with the wind.

To succeed with the annual SWEET PEA, be sure to get an early start, so that they may give you weeks of bloom before hot weather. This may be done by very early planting outdoors or, better yet, by starting them indoors in individual pots from which they may be easily moved. Plant in a depression, so that they will catch all water, and set the plants at least six inches apart. Have strings ready so that the first tendrils will find support. Seed-forming will stop the blooming. There is on the market a special soil inoculation for Sweet Peas that seems to help. Semishade is best in the Middlewest.

A native that resembles Sweet Pea is *bulbosa* (not illustrated). It has fragrant, rather small, pink flowers, and bulbs as big as a man's thumb. American Indians used them as we use Potato, but American farmers fight this plant as a spreading perennial weed.

HOG PEANUT is another weed Pea that persists until every one of its tiny tubers is dug out. It has small lavender flowers followed by regulation pods. But just below the ground it bears a colorless blossom that develops into a pear-shaped pod with one large nut in it. And until either you or the hogs dig out this nut the vine will persist, to bother your shade garden.

WISTERIA is one of the world's most beautiful flowering vines, with pink or lavender flower clusters many feet long in its choice forms. None of the seedlings are worth buying. Insist upon grafted plants.

SENNA PEA is a dainty white-flowering vine grown in greenhouses for winter bouquet material.

WILD SENNA is a striking subject for the back of the border. In August each of its stems turns into a yellow plume of bloom. This lasts for a month and is followed by picturesque brown pods. It is absolutely hardy.

At the same season, the roadsides are yellow with the bloom of PARTRIDGE PEA, its little sister. Its delicate petals defy the heat, but its green leaves fold shut when touched, giving it the name of Sensitive-Plant. An annual that selfsows, it can become a pest in pastures. Animals that graze upon it are made sick.

There are many, many other wild Peas. Also of this family but not illustrated are Alfalfa, *Amorpha* (Lead-Plant), Clovers, *Cytisus* (Broom), *Dolichos* (Hyacinth Bean), *Galega* (Goats Rue), *Mimosa* (Sensitive-Plant), *Pueraria* (Kudzu-Vine), and Soybean.

56

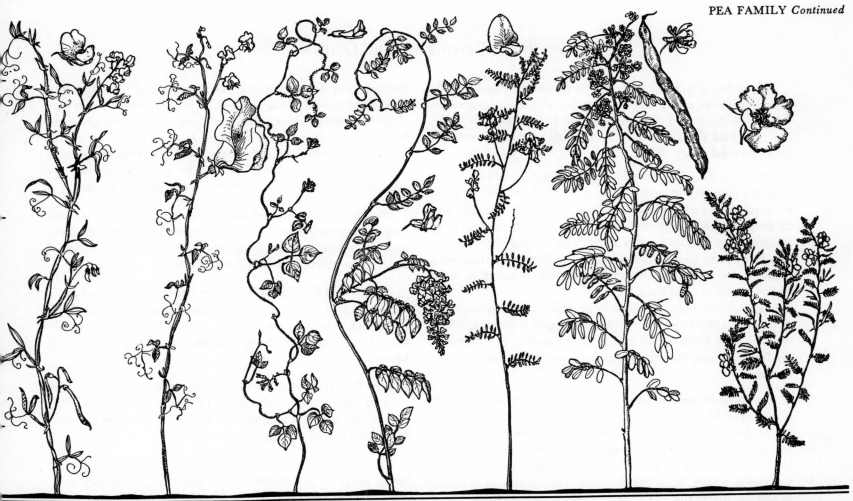

PERENNIAL PEA
Lathyrus latifolius
(lath'-i-rus)

SWEET PEA
Lathyrus odoratus

HOG PEANUT
Amphicarpa
(am-fi-kahr'-pah)

WISTERIA
Wistaria
(Wis-tee'-ri-ah)

SENNA PEA
Swainsona galegifolia
(swayn-soh'-nah)

WILD SENNA
Cassia marilandica

PARTRIDGE PEA
Cassia Chamaecrista
(cash'-i-a)

Flax, Geranium, and Oxalis

It is rather a surprise to find that plants with such widely differing leaves are closely related, but the resemblance this time is in the flower. Compare single blossoms of each and you will find the same five, frail petals set loosely and enclosing a seed ovary.

Of course FLAX is only a cousin of the Geraniums, but it is worth claiming in any family, since for hundreds of years its tough flexible fibers have clothed the world. The oil from its seeds mixes our paints. In our perennial border its gray foliage and soft blue flowers serve to harmonize clashing colors, just as the blue of the sky does for flowers in their wild settings. Its habit of frequent selfsowing supplies us with young plants at all seasons.

Commercial Flax, which furnishes linen and linseed oil, differs but little from the garden form, and a morning drive through Flax fields is like looking at the ocean. The blue petals fall by noon, but numerous buds are ready for the next morning.

A beloved house plant the world over is the HORSESHOE GERANIUM, so called because of the shadowy, dark marking of that shape on many of the round leaves. The ancients loved it so much that they gave it a legend of miraculous birth. Their story is that the prophet Mohammed, when bathing in a lake, hung his garment over a common Mallow. When he lifted the garment, the Mallow had turned to a Geranium!

Quite as marvelous is the real story of how the horticulturists worked with the common single Geranium until its stamens had developed into extra petals and its colors covered every tone of pink and red. It is easily grown from cuttings because its thick stems are packed with enough plant food to make it root and bloom in sand or water. Of course it eventually requires added fertility. Do not make the mistake of feeding it too well, however, or it will become so busy producing leaves and stems that it will forget to bloom.

Having quickly learned that it was being grown from cuttings rather than seeds, the Geranium now rarely produces one of the long pointed pods that gave it the genus name of *Pelargonium,* which means "stork's bill."

In our WILD GERANIUM, or Cranesbill, the pod has a clever trick of throwing its seeds afar. Examine one and figure it out. The various kinds of Wild Geranium are easily moved into our gardens and, among them, furnish all-season bloom.

The OXALIS cousins take their name from the oxalic acid in their bulbs and leaves. In the tropics, where they "take" the lawns as Dandelions do ours, their bulbs are used for food much as we use Cranberries.

The BUTTERCUP OXALIS makes a pretty winter house plant or a summer border plant for semishady locations. The same bulbs cannot be used for both, however, as they require a good long dormant period between blooms.

Geraniums with fragrant leaves, such as the ROSE GERANIUM of our grandmothers, are having new popularity.

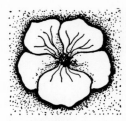

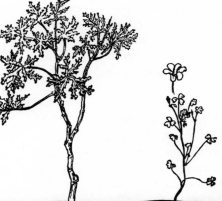

PERENNIAL FLAX
Linum perenne
(ly'-num)

WILD GERANIUM
Geranium maculatum
(jee-ray'-ni-um)

HORSESHOE GERANIUM
Pelargonium
(pel-ahr-goh'-ni-um)

ROSE GERANIUM
Pelargonium graveolens

YELLOW OXALIS
Oxalis stricta
(ok'-sah-lis)

BUTTERCUP OXALIS
Oxalis cernua

HERONSBILL
Erodium
(e-roh'-di-um)

59

Spurges with Flower-like Leaves

This milky-juiced family varies from prickly curiosities to the dignified Poinsettia. Whatever shape or size one assumes, you will recognize it by the plump little seed box that perches at the tip of each pistil. The colorful parts are not petals but showy specialized leaves!

Beware careless tasting or handling, for many are poisonous. Yet the tuberous roots of one species furnish our popular dessert, tapioca.

The CASTOR-BEAN, parent of castor oil, is thought of more kindly as the annual that can make quick background or screen plantings. It is only a cousin of the *Euphorbia* but has the same milky juice and plump three-parted seed container. This container is covered with green prickles. Notice how the staminate flowers are in a fluffy mass several inches below the pistilate ones. This is usually a sign that a plant is fertilized by wasps, since they work down a stem, while bees begin at the bottom and work up.

We all know POINSETTIA, the Christmas flower. The true flowers will be found near the center of the flaming red bracts. They are little green vases, no larger than peas, and each one carries on its side a brimming-over honey jar. The vase is filled with a bunch of stamens, from which stretches the typical pistil with seed pod on its tip. In Mexico, where it is a native plant, the Poinsettia grows as tall as the houses, but in the greenhouse it may be made to bloom at any height. You can grow it yourself if you let it rest, desert dry, for months after blooming. If you use it as a cut flower, remember to sear the stem ends because of their milky juice.

The clear green and white foliage of SNOW-ON-THE-MOUNTAIN looks so refreshing along the roadways that we invited it into our flower gardens until we discovered that it had a dangerous pollen irritating to eyes and tender skins and poisonous to fish if it blows into the pool.

FLOWERING SPURGE is the Wild Baby's Breath of the roadsides. Its flowers have wide commercial use because they will stand up in the hottest weather. Many an honest penny has been earned by gathering them. The plants like to cling to clay slopes, and where grading has been done, one may often trace their water-seeking roots eight or ten feet down, showing how they withstand drouth. Once established in your garden they are hard to kill.

RUGWEED is under foot almost everywhere in late summer, spreading its red-green leaves like a fan. SPOTTED SPURGE is its upright form.

CYPRESS SPURGE has foliage like short sprays of the evergreen from which it takes its name. It is often found in old cemeteries, where it remains green throughout the worst drouths. It is a bad spreader in gardens.

For our window gardens there is another group that would easily pass for Cacti if a pinprick did not reveal their milky juice. Most of them are plump, some as round as balls, but one of them stretches out slender, thorny branches, which give it the name CROWN-OF-THORNS. All of these require desert conditions to thrive.

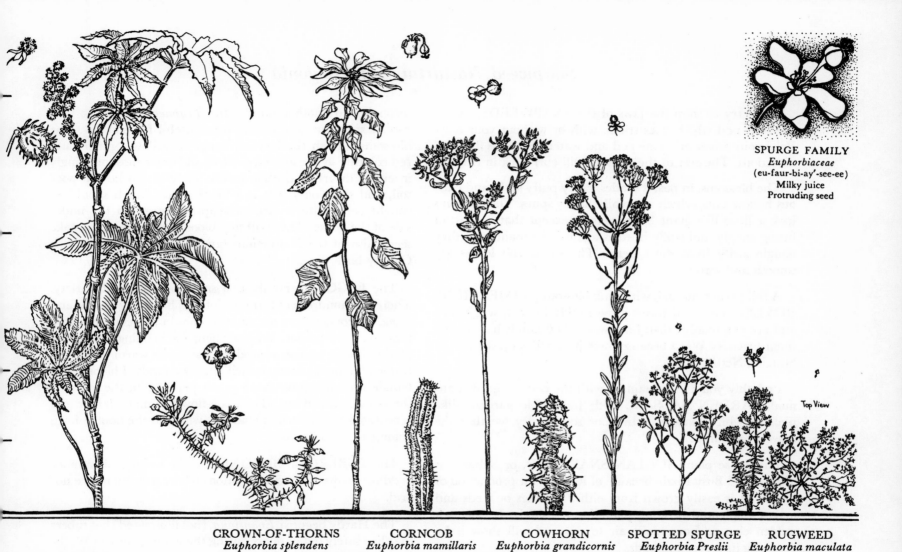

SPURGE FAMILY
Euphorbiaceae
(eu-faur-bi-ay'-see-ee)
Milky juice
Protruding seed

Top View

CROWN-OF-THORNS
Euphorbia splendens

CORNCOB
Euphorbia mamillaris

COWHORN
Euphorbia grandicornis

SPOTTED SPURGE
Euphorbia Preslii

RUGWEED
Euphorbia maculata

CASTOR-BEAN
Ricinus communis
(ris'-i-nus)

POINSETTIA
Euphorbia pulcherrima

SNOW-ON-THE-
MOUNTAIN
Euphorbia marginata
(eu-faur'-bi-ah)

FLOWERING SPURGE
Euphorbia corollata

CYPRESS SPURGE
Euphorbia Cyparissias

61

Snapweed, Nasturtium, and Begonia

Don't try to snap the jaws of the SNAPWEEDS, for it's the seed pod which does tricks, with or without your help. Poke your finger at a ripe pod and watch the seeds fly in all directions. The rest of the capsule will curl back in ringlets.

The blossoms, in pastel shades, carry puffy sacks and curious hollow tails, which are really honey spurs. The blossoms look a little like giant Snapdragons, except that instead of fitting snugly and stiffly in rows against the main stalk they dangle airily from short stems. The stems and leaves are smooth and watery.

A tall garden annual, with pink blossoms, is IMPATIENS ROYLEI. The wild forms grow rankly in cool, wet woods and are commonly called Jewelweed. Our family has dubbed them Friendly Weed because their juice will stop the itch of Stinging Nettle.

Probably you are acquainted with the beloved garden annual GARDEN BALSAM, with its double gardenia-like pink or white blossoms. In poor soil or dry weather the flowers are single.

The house plant SULTAN SNAPWEED, or Sultana, is often called Busy Lizzie because of its constant production of bloom. It is easily grown from either cuttings or seeds and makes a splendid bedding plant for hot shade. It resents a sudden change from moist air to dry and will show it by dropping its leaves and buds.

NASTURTIUM, resembling the Snapweeds in its watery leaves and stems and in its extended honey spur, fools us by belonging to another family, the *Tropaeolaceae*. The seed cannot snap but is in a solid form, useful for pickling. The blossoms furnish the loveliest range of yellow, orange, and red coloring in our annual gardens and come most obligingly in either dwarf or trailing forms. They bloom best in poor soil, and their only pest is a black aphis, which should be caught early with a nicotine-soapsuds spray on the under side of the leaves. They will stop blooming if allowed to make seed. Also of the Nasturtium family, but not illustrated, is Canary-bird Vine.

The BEGONIA family is a small one of great variety. There are hundreds of forms of foliage, blooming habits, and roots. Of course there are no wild ones in this country, since they are very tender. We use them for bedding and house plants, where we can reproduce the moist warm air of the tropics. On most plants you will find two kinds of bloom. The female type will have small petals perched on the top of a three-winged seed box. The male flower is much larger and is centered by a bunch of stamens, which in the double form change to extra petals.

The TUBEROUS BEGONIAS make wonderful summer bedding plants in shaded locations where conditions are not arid.

The Hardy Begonia, *Evansiana*, (not illustrated) has tubers that live safely out of doors during the winter, south of Washington, D. C. By careful mulching they sometimes do so in the North, but it is better to keep them inside and run no risk of losing such garden treasures.

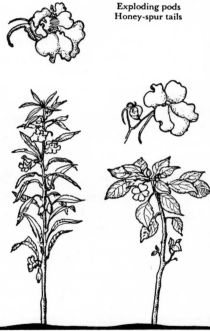

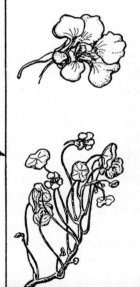

BALSAM FAMILY
Balsaminaceae
(ball-sam-i-nay'-see-ee)
Exploding pods
Honey-spur tails

BEGONIA FAMILY
Begoniaceae
(be-goh-ni-ay'-see-ee)
Showy foliage
Male and female flowers

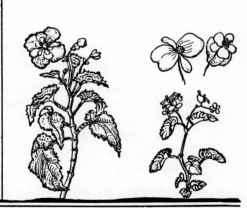

IMPATIENS ROYLEI
Impatiens Roylei
(im-pay'-shi-enz)

PALE SNAPWEED
Impatiens pallida

GARDEN BALSAM
Impatiens Balsamina

SULTAN SNAPWEED
Impatiens Sultani

NASTURTIUM
Tropaeolum majus
(troh-pee'-oh-lum)

TUBEROUS BEGONIA
Begonia tuberhybrida
(be-goh'-ni-ah)

PERPETUAL BEGONIA
Begonia semperflorens

The Showy Mallows

Malvaceae, the family name, means mucilaginous, or sticky. Its varied species show many adaptations of this quality, and that of producing fibers.

This is the sort of family which, if human, would be the backbone of the community. It is a lavish provider of food, clothing, and beauty and contains no poisonous members. It has traveled the world over, except for the Arctic zones, but under all conditions has retained its old-fashioned hoop-skirt blossoms, which children delight in using for ladies in their play-pretend garden parties.

Each member of the Mallow tribe, be he brother or distant cousin, wears the peculiar club-like pistil protruding from the middle of the blossom and grown about with stamens. This is attached to the base of the petals, so that it drops with the faded flowers. There is considerable variation, however, in the seed forms. Often, as in the Hollyhock, the seeds are in round, uncovered "cheeses."

HOLLYHOCKS remind us of English cottage gardens, but they never saw England until they were brought over from the Holy Land by returning Crusaders. That is how they acquired the name Holy-hock. A wild form has roots that furnish the gummy substance used for making marshmallow candy.

MALLOW MARVELS will be found in your seed catalogue rather than in your botany book, for they have only recently been developed from the wild Rose Mallow. They are gorgeous perennial subjects for background planting, preferring a moist situation. Their white and pink blooms fill the gap when Hollyhocks fade in late summer.

A good example of the family's tendency to have tough, fibrous stems is found in VELVET-LEAF. We consider it a bad weed in our cornfields, but in China it is a cultivated crop, being used as the backing material for nearly all Chinese rugs.

OKRA, or Gumbo, has the oddest pods of all. They look much like green Bananas. The young pods are cut into small sections and added to soups for thickening. The plant was brought from Africa in the days of slave trading. Northern summers are often too short to allow it to mature.

Two useful pink flowers for the late summer are the miniature hollyhocks Checkerbloom and TREE MALLOW. Only the former is perennial.

FLOWERING MAPLE, a tropical plant, is popular for winter windows and summer porches, as it is practically everblooming. It comes in both single and double forms and in a wide range of colors.

POPPY MALLOW, or Buffalo Rose, was called "man root" by the Indians because of its enormous roots, sometimes branching like arms and legs. In these roots it stores food and moisture to insure its life on the arid prairies, and it often drapes its crimson-flowered vines from sheer clay precipices.

Also of this family but not illustrated are *Hibiscus Trionum* (Flower-of-an-Hour), *Malvastrum coccineum* (Red False Mallow), Cotton, and Roselle.

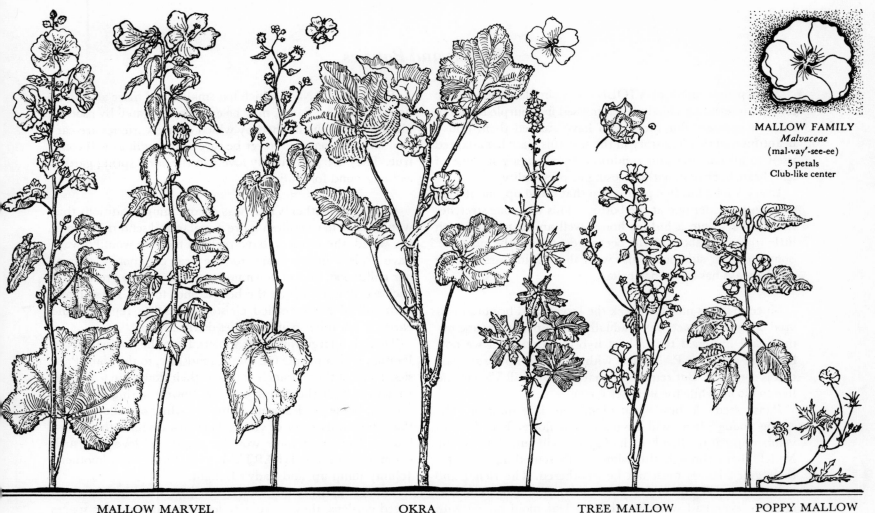

MALLOW FAMILY
Malvaceae
(mal-vay'-see-ee)
5 petals
Club-like center

MALLOW MARVEL
Hibiscus Moscheutos
(hy-bis'-cus)

OKRA
Hibiscus esculentus

TREE MALLOW
Lavatera
(lav-ah-tee'-rah)

POPPY MALLOW
Callirhoë
(kal-ir'-oh-ee)

HOLLYHOCK
Althaea rosea
(al-thee'-ah)

VELVET-LEAF
Abutilon Theophrasti

PRAIRIE MALLOW
Sidalcea
(si-dal'-se-ah)

FLOWERING MAPLE
Abutilon hybridum
(ah-beu'-ti-lon)

65

Violets and Pansies

Most people think of VIOLETS as simple, modest little flowers, interesting chiefly when massed in a purple bunch to make a corsage. But those who have studied them find a beautiful and thrilling story in the way this plant has adapted itself to all climates and conditions by changing its type of leaf, branch, or root, without losing its personality.

Every Violet has five petals, two that stand up, one at each side, and a wider one at the bottom. This wide one stretches its base back into a hidden honey well and is marked with little road signs showing the bees where to find the entrance. Sometimes the side petals also wear those guidelines and the pistil always has an orange collar.

Since the bees naturally seek the largest and brightest colored blooms, the race was gradually built up, and in time human skill hastened the task of hybridization until we now have the gorgeous PANSIES, without which no spring garden is complete. But remember that they are still Violets and like to bloom while the weather is cool.

Pansy seeds do best when planted in late summer. The strong young plants will have set their flower buds by November and at the first breath of spring will burst into bloom. Mulch them through the winter with something airy, for their green leaves must not be smothered. The richer and moister the soil, the larger your blossoms will be. The best ones we ever had were in a bed of leaf mold mixed with rotted cow manure. Occasionally a few plants will live over their second winter, but to be sure of a supply you should sow seed each August.

TUFTED PANSY, which has smaller and more abundant flowers than the Pansy, may be easily propagated by root division. This is the method by which choice varieties are carried on, since one can never be sure that seedlings will come true. They are particularly lovely in the early spring garden as foreground for Tulips.

While the mother Violet was encouraging conditions that would make her children more popular and send them up in the world, she seems to have realized that we would always have a place in our hearts for the dear common Violets of our childhood, and so down under the leaves she grows little enclosed flowers, which the bees cannot touch. These make pods full of seeds (called cleistogamous) to replenish the earth. A few other plant families do the same.

There is a large variety of Violets, from the tiny wild baby Pansies, which purple the Ozark roadsides, to the giant Pansies. Some of them branch and bear their flowers in leaf axils. In others both the leaves and the flowers spring from the ground. Some are fragrant. Some are white or yellow rather than the family color of violet. They always have the almost human faces that have won for them our love and such common names as HEART'S-EASE, Little Grandmothers, Johnny-jump-up, and Lady's Delight.

Though many wild Violets are bad spreaders in cultivated gardens, they make excellent ground cover for spaces under trees and for the north sides of buildings where nothing else will grow. Their clever way of pinching their seeds out of their pods sometimes shoots them as far as fifteen feet.

VIOLET FAMILY
Violaceae
(vy-o-lay'-see-ee)
Petal-face
Honey spur

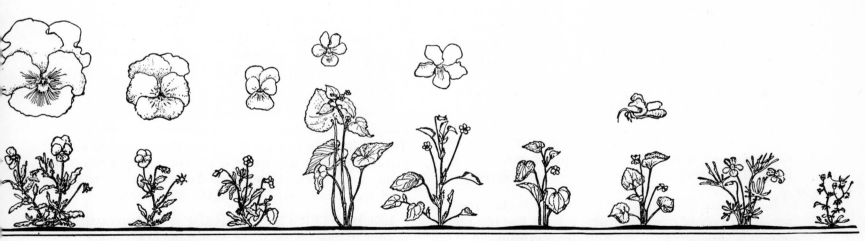

HEART'S-EASE
Viola tricolor

CANADA VIOLET
Viola canadensis

YELLOW VIOLET
Viola pubescens

BIRD-FOOT VIOLET
Viola pedata

PANSY
Viola tricolor
(vy-oh'-lah)

TUFTED PANSY
Viola cornuta

CREAM VIOLET
Viola striata

BUTTERFLY VIOLET
Viola papilionacea

BABY HEART'S-EASE
Viola Rafinesquii

Flowers That Count Their Parts by Fours

When you find a flower with four rather large petals sitting on top of a long seed container, it probably belongs to the Evening-Primrose Family. Examine the tip of the pistil to make sure. It should be divided into four parts. The buds are long and pointed and completely covered by the four calyx lobes, which turn back against the stem when the flower opens.

The yellow biennial EVENING-PRIMROSE is found all over the United States. Along hot roadsides the flowers are small, but in rich garden soil they become large. It has been given a prominent place in European gardens, and surely no flower is more dramatic in its opening. Like glamorous night-club ladies its blossoms wait for exactly the right light effects in sunset colors, then suddenly throw back their green cloaks and swirl wide the skirts of their golden evening gowns.

The name *Oenothera* means "wine-scented," and when the heady fragrance of these flowers floats across the garden, the night moths quickly gather. They collect a bit of pollen-dusted web from the throat of each flower and carry it on to the next plant, for the plants make sure of cross-pollination by usually opening only one flower apiece each evening.

Rose-colored BLOOMING SALLY, or Willow Herb, is sometimes called Fireweed because it is the first plant to return to burned-over timberland. Its seeds explain why it can travel so fast and far, for they have airy wings similar to those of Milkweed seeds. The seed capsules are long and slender.

FUCHSIA is a house plant witn us. Its pointed sepals are usually white or pink. Our grandmothers called it Flora's-Eardrops. Always keep it in cool semishade. If placed for the summer in a northeast exposure, near a pool, it will bloom constantly. It loves moist air, and when that condition is combined with moderate temperatures, as on our West Coast, it lives out of doors the year around and becomes a small tree.

Two favorite pink garden annuals are the CLARKIA and GODETIA. Both are natives of the West Coast, the former from Oregon, where its single form was discovered and named for Clark of the Lewis and Clark expedition, and the latter from the mountains of California. Both do best in cool climates. Under favorable conditions Godetia makes a colorful bedding plant. It is widely used for that purpose in England.

SUNDROPS look very much like the Evening-Primrose except that they are not so tall and remain open all day. Their yellow blossoms are so gay and the plants such an unpresuming height that we do not resent the slight spreading habit of their roots. They are good perennials for the hardy border, especially useful for filling in odd corners.

ENCHANTER'S NIGHTSHADE is a very unenchanting weed with insignificant white flowers and beggar's-lice seeds. But tradition says it was used in witches' brew. We rarely see it because it haunts woodland thickets rather than troubling our gardens.

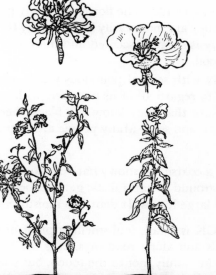

EVENING-PRIMROSE FAMILY
Onagraceae
(oh-nah-gray'-see-ee)
Flower parts in 4's
Large seed pod below

BLOOMING SALLY
Epilobium angustifolium
(ep-i-loh'-bi-um)

CLARKIA
Clarkia elegans
(klahr'-ki-ah)

GODETIA
Godetia
(goh-dee'-shi-ah)

EVENING-PRIMROSE
Oenothera biennis
(ee-noh-thee'-rah)

FUCHSIA
Fuchsia
(feu'-shi-ah)

SUNDROPS
Oenothera fruticosa

**ENCHANTER'S
NIGHTSHADE**
Circaea lutetiana
(sur-see'-ah)

69

The Cut-Leaved Carrots

The family name *Umbelliferae* describes the way in which the members of this family arrange their tiny white or yellow blossoms. It seems to be a cooperative plan for attracting and supporting their favorite insects, one of which is the beautiful black swallowtail butterfly, whose eggs produce the green and scarlet caterpillar that feeds on the plants.

All these plants have hollow stems, and leaves that are more or less divided and fern-like. The flowers of many genera are so similar that they are more easily identified by their seeds. The entire family is strongly scented and more useful for flavoring than for food.

Since this is a family with several poisonous plants, children should be taught to regard all of its members with suspicion until they are sure that they know the black sheep. This applies to root, leaf, and seed. Many people are allergic even to Celery.

COW-PARSNIP is a coarse but showy native plant sometimes used in the background of naturalistic gardens because of its great height and large leaves. It demands moisture.

WATER HEMLOCK is a tall, foul-smelling plant often seen in boggy lowlands and along roadways. It is the most poisonous member of the family, not to the touch, but when its root or seed is eaten. Poison Hemlock (not illustrated) is a similar plant.

SANICLE, or Black Snakeroot, is a harmless weed with seeds of the beggar's-lice type. Such seeds are usually covered with hooked prickles and are distributed by clinging to people's clothing and the fur of animals.

SEA-HOLLY, a perennial, is valued mostly as a source of winter bouquet material. For this use it should be cut and dried, as its burs, bracts, and stems turn blue.

Queen Anne's Lace is the romantic name given to the WILD CARROT, from which our garden vegetable was developed many hundreds of years ago. The name comes from the lace-patterned, white flower, but farmers give the name Devil's-Plague to the same plant because it is an almost uncontrollable weed in the East. It is mistaken hospitality to entertain it on our premises. When dry, the seed head curls into the shape of a bird's nest.

BLUE LACE-FLOWER has found a place in our annual gardens because of its lacy form and dainty coloring, but it does not endure hot weather well.

SWEET CICELY is pretty in wild gardens, and its leaves when crushed give the fragrance of Anise. Its roots are considered edible but are best avoided unless you are very sure that you "know your carrots."

GOUTWEED, or Bishops-Weed, with its variegated green and white foliage is a favorite ground cover for moist, shady places. Its lacy white flowers are secondary in importance. It is a rampant and inconsiderate spreader, so think carefully before giving it the key to your garden.

This family ranks second only to the Mint Family in the role of providing seasoning for our foods. Here we find Dill, Caraway, Coriander, Anise, Chervil, Cumin, Lovage, Celery, Parsley, and Angelica, none of which are illustrated.

8 ft.

To 5 ft.

CARROT FAMILY
Umbelliferae
(um-be-lif'-er-ee)
Flowers in umbrellas
Cut foliage

COW-PARSNIP
Heracleum lanatum
(her-ah-klee'-um)

SANICLE
Sanicula canadensis
(say-nik'-u-lah)

WILD CARROT
Daucus Carota
(dau'-kus)

SWEET CICELY
Osmorhiza longistylis
(os-moh-ry'-zah)

WATER HEMLOCK
Cicuta maculata
(sy-key'-tah)

SEA-HOLLY
Eryngium maritimum
(e-rin'-ji-um)

BLUE LACE-FLOWER
Trachymene caerulea
(tray-ki-mee'-nee)

GOUTWEED
Aegopodium
(ee-goh-poh'-di-um)

The Primroses

Primulaceae means "first" and suggests the very early-flowering habit of the wild Primroses of Europe. Do not confuse this family with our Evening-Primroses, which are no relation at all and whose flowers have only four petals instead of the five of *Primulaceae*.

The botanical points are a little too complicated for this book, but the family is small enough for you to remember its common members. They all love shade, coolness, and moisture, but not swampy conditions.

The LOOSESTRIFES are attractive natives with yellow blossoms. WHORLED LOOSESTRIFE especially deserves a place in the garden. Its prolific flowers are carried distinctively in the axils of the leaves all up the stem.

SHOOTING STAR, another native, holds its pink, white, or lavender flowers upside down! This trait has suggested the nicknames of Wild Cyclamen and Bird's-bill. In some form it is native to every state of the Union. It is easily moved during its dormant period in late summer.

The aristocratic CYCLAMEN we buy at the greenhouse. In its native Persia it is given the name of Sowbread because it is so plentiful that its roasted tubers are fed to pigs! Alas, it does not grow so easily in our homes. But if given a temperature of fifty degrees at night and not more than seventy degrees by day, a very light window, and no water standing in its saucer, it will bloom all winter. It must be put in a cool place in summer and the bulb must never be entirely dried, for its leaves are evergreen. Easily grown from seed, it will bloom in fifteen months. You will think them slow in coming up until you learn that they grow their bulbs before their leaves. There are hardy species from Europe for late summer bloom in distinguished rock gardens.

Wild PRIMROSES are so numerous in England as to be weeds and are used to make Cowslip wine in the same way that we make wine from Dandelions. In this country they are considered garden aristocrats and humored with moist though well-drained soil, high shade, and special pre-winter care. Plants do better when divided frequently. Their seeds are small and slow to germinate except when very fresh. The flowers come in a wide assortment of colors. Some are born in clusters or whorls, carried on single stems, while others spread their beauty over many short stems, all springing from a single crown. Besides the hardy perennial garden Primroses, there are many tender greenhouse sorts.

The PIMPERNEL is an annual found in many gardens because of its bright flowers, which usually run to reds. It is called the Poor Mans Weather-glass because of its habit of closing its flowers a half an hour before a rain.

The most common member of this family is the shade-loving trailer with yellow star blossoms, which you will call MONEYWORT or Creeping Charlie according to where you were brought up. It is useful where nothing else will grow but is a rampant spreader, so do not let it get started among choice plants, where it will make trouble in the future.

HORLED LOOSESTRIFE
Lysimachia quadrifolia
(ly-si-may'-ki-ah)

SHOOTING STAR
Dodecatheon
(doh-de-kath'-e-on)

FAIRY PRIMROSE
Primula malacoides
(prim'-eu-lah)

PIMPERNEL
Anagallis
(an-ah-gal'-is)

FRINGED LOOSESTRIFE
Steironema ciliatum
(sty-roh-nee'-mah)

CYCLAMEN
Cyclamen
(sik'-lah-men)

POLYANTHUS PRIMROSE
Primula polyantha

MONEYWORT
Lysimachia Nummularia

Gentians and Some Winter Bouquet Material

The Gentian Family is named for an ancient king who discovered that their roots were medicinal. They love cool, moist situations. In England they grow so rampantly that they have to be controlled. Most of them are a richer and deeper blue than is found in any other native flower. The leaves are opposite and the flowers tubular.

The FRINGED GENTIAN, of which the poets sing, is a biennial. It is almost impossible to transplant because of its long taproot. Some nurseries specializing in native plant material sell young plants raised in pots. If you wish to try your luck at raising your own, remember that the seed germinates slowly unless very fresh. If you start with a blooming-sized (potted) plant, you may tuck the fresh-picked seed about the base of the mother plant and transplant seedlings as soon as true leaves appear. The flowers open at the end of summer.

ROSE GENTIAN, a pink hardy annual of the western plains, is much more easily handled. Its seeds sown in the fall will spring up and give abundant bloom the next summer.

The CLOSED GENTIAN, or Bottle Gentian, is fairly common in moist, sunny meadows. Although its bells remain stubbornly shut, they are vividly blue and in large clusters. They are beautiful either for gardens or for cut flowers. Bumblebees refuse to respect the closed door and force an opening. The plants are easily moved, and you may enjoy experimenting with the seeds.

The PRAIRIE GENTIAN, now found rarely in the few existing patches of native prairie, was once very plentiful and was beloved by pioneer women. It is the last flower of summer, for even in October it opens on sunny days. When closed, its bell is rusty green, but when it opens, it displays five intensely blue points, between which are claws of a paler shade.

The Leadwort Family gives us a little group of tubular flowers unlike each other and showing little resemblance to their closest relative, the Primrose. They take their name from the fact that the roots of some members of the family stain the fingers as lead would. They include no food plants.

SEA-LAVENDER, an easily grown perennial, makes large masses of misty bloom and is sometimes called Lavender Baby's Breath. Try drying it for winter bouquets and also the annual varieties *Limonium sinuatum* and *Limonium Suworowi* (not illustrated).

THRIFT does not dry well, but its tufted foliage and pink balls of bloom are good in the rock garden.

PLUMBAGO rivals the Gentians in intense blueness. Because of its late summer blooming habit, as well as its beauty of flower and bronze-green foliage, it should be in every perennial garden. In some sections of the country its invading roots make it a pest, while in others it tends to winterkill and is therefore rated as a choice aristocrat. If you live in the latter section, try keeping a few plants during the winter in a box of dirt in the cellar or in a cold frame. You may make root cuttings easily in the spring.

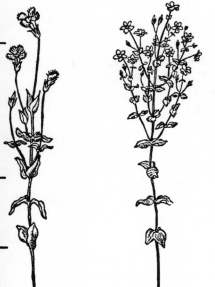

GENTIAN FAMILY
Gentianaceae
(jen-shi-ah-nay'-see-ee)
Tube flowers
Opposite leaves

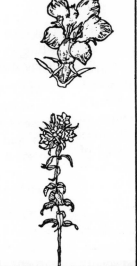

LEADWORT FAMILY
Plumbaginaceae
(plum-baj-i-nay'-see-ee)

ROSE GENTIAN
Sabatia
(sa-bat'-i-ah)

PRAIRIE GENTIAN
Gentiana calycosa

THRIFT
Statice Armeria
(stat'-i-see)

RINGED GENTIAN
Gentiana crinita
(jen-she-ay'-na)

CLOSED GENTIAN
Gentiana Andrewsii

SEA-LAVENDER
Limonium latifolium
(li-moh'-ni-um)

PLUMBAGO
Ceratostigma
(ser-ah-toh-stig'-mah)

75

The Glossy-Leaved Dogbanes

Bane means poison, and this entire family should be regarded with suspicion. Drugs and insecticides are prepared from some tropical varieties, one of which is the Ordeal Tree of Madagascar, said to be the most poisonous plant in existence.

The family is very closely related to the Milkweed Family, having the same milky juice and pods opening along one side only. These Dogbane pods are unique in that they are all borne in distinctive forked pairs.

OLEANDER is a tropical tree that we grow in tubs for the sake of its waxy pink and white blossoms. Its leaves, stems, and flowers are poisonous if eaten, and even its wood, accidentally used as meat skewers, is known to have killed a number of people. Ancient literature tells of attempts to eradicate it from the Mediterranean region, where it grows wild, because of its danger to animals. It is also a carrier of scale and other insect pests. In spite of all this the world continues to make a place for its beauty. Plants should be well fed while in flower, then pruned and rested.

A native plant with pale blue flowers and slender glossy leaves is the AMSONIA, sometimes used in large-scale garden borders. The foliage is always attractive, and especially so in the autumn, when it turns a clear yellow. The flowers are not notably showy, though in a sunny wild garden they form an effective background for Blue-eyed Grass, which blooms at the same time and is the same color.

HEMP DOGBANE is often called Indian Hemp because the American Indians use its tough bark for making ropes. There is another, more spreading variety with pale pink bells shaped like those of Lily-of-the-Valley. At a casual glance you would guess Dogbanes to be Milkweeds, because of their thick milky leaves. The conspicuous difference lies in the shape of the blossoms. Dogbanes have bells, while the Milkweeds have hourglasses.

A favorite tender vine for window boxes and hanging baskets is the BIGLEAF PERIWINKLE. Its mottled green and white leaves are showy, but it rarely develops its blue flowers. Bring it into the house for the winter.

MADAGASCAR PERIWINKLE, the nontrailing member of the Periwinkle genus, is a favorite bedding annual because of its constant blooming habit and its ability to resist heat and drouth. The white-flowered one suggests Orange blossoms in the beautiful contrast of its white flowers and vivid green leaves but it lacks their fragrance. This type is often used as a house plant.

COMMON PERIWINKLE, or Grave Myrtle, is a hardy native of Europe that finds, or makes, itself at home by spreading its glossy evergreen leaves over shady banks in our gardens. Its blue blossoms are shaped exactly like those of the single Oleander. It is adapted to many useful purposes, such as serving as a lawn in places where grass will not grow, as a ground cover under trees, or where bulbs may poke through to bloom later.

DOGBANE FAMILY
Apocynaceae
(ah-pos-i-nay'-see-ee)
Phlox-like flowers
Thick, glossy leaves

AMSONIA
Amsonia
(am-soh'-ni-ah)

BIGLEAF PERIWINKLE
Vinca major
(vin'-ka)

PERIWINKLE
Vinca minor

OLEANDER
Nerium Oleander
(nee'-ri-um)

HEMP DOGBANE
Apocynum cannabinum
(ah-pos'-i-num)

MADAGASCAR PERIWINKLE
Vinca rosea

77

Milkweeds with Down-Filled Pods

The members of this family are named *Asclepias* for the Greek god of medicine, which shows that the ancients regarded it as an important drug source. There is still a market for the dried roots of many of its varieties. It has no other commercial value, though scientists tell us that use could be made of its stem fibers, which are stronger and smoother than those of Hemp and would make good binder twine. It also has possibilities as a source of rubber, and experiments are being made to test it for commercial production.

As you might expect from their popular family name, most members have milky juice. They also have a peculiar kind of seed pod, correctly called a follicle, since it opens on only one side. Provided with silky parachutes, the seeds travel by air in fair weather, but should rain force them down they can travel on water too, for each seed has a corky edge that makes it a boat. No wonder the farmers find them so hard to control.

Even stranger than its seeds are its blossoms, half up and half down, each with a central crown holding a rich store of honey. To obtain this honey the bees and butterflies must swing below. Their legs, clasping the blossom for support, slip into narrow openings from which they cannot escape without dragging with them little bags of waxy pollen. Sometimes you will find dead insects that hadn't the strength to pull loose.

WAX-PLANT is a beloved window vine of slow growth. Each star-like pink blossom carries a glistening drop of honey in its heart. Each year the flower clusters spring from the old blossom spurs, which should never be removed. The thick glossy leaves appreciate frequent washing.

SWAMP MILKWEED is a perennial that grows best with its feet in water. Farmers destroy it by draining the land, but many gardeners make a place for its attractive pink flowers. It is the one which could be used as a fiber crop.

COMMON MILKWEED is a pest in grainfields but a thing of beauty with its fragrant umbels of purple-pink bloom and its great leaves that are waxy above and downy below. Its young shoots are sometimes eaten as greens, and Indians produced sugar by shaking the honey dew from its blooms in early morning and drying it. Its pods are large, showy, and very ornamental for winter bouquets. CLIMBING MILKWEED is a fence row pest.

BUTTERFLY-WEED differs from its brothers not only in its vivid orange color but in the fact that it is not milky. It prefers poor, sandy soil, and florists collect its bloom from the roadside, where it does better than in cultivation. It is valued by gardeners in Europe, by butterflies the world over, and by children who use the flowers for "British Red Coats" in flower battles. As its ancient name, Pleurisy-Root, implies, it was used as a remedy for lung trouble.

Along every roadside in autumn you will find the dust-pale flowers of the dwarf HORSE-TAIL MILKWEED.

Also of this family but not illustrated are *Stapelia* (Carrion-Flower or Blood-Flower) and *Ceropegia* (Rosary Vine).

78

MILKWEED FAMILY
Asclepiadaceae
(as-klee-pi-a-day'-see-ee)
Hourglass flowers
Milky juice

WAX-PLANT
Hoya carnosa
(hoi'-ah)

SWAMP MILKWEED
Asclepias incarnata
(as-klee'-pi-as)

COMMON MILKWEED
Asclepias syriaca

CLIMBING MILKWEED
Gonolobus laevis
(goh-nol'-oh-bus)

BUTTERFLY-WEED
Asclepias tuberosa

HORSE-TAIL MILKWEED
Asclepias verticillata

79

Morning-Glories

First place on this page should by rights go to the Sweet Potato, the one useful member of the family. But we could not find a blossom to draw. From years of being propagated only by sprouts, the plant has learned that flowers and seeds are superfluous! However, news of a discovery comes from Louisiana. If the Sweet Potato vine is half-girdled near its base, twice, on opposite sides of the stalk and half an inch apart, it may burst into bloom! This is worth trying in your window garden.

Of course you know a Morning-Glory blossom when you see one, but had you noticed the five stiff little tracks on which the bees may safely travel down to the honey supply without tearing the fragile blossom? See how cleverly, too, the flower is folded into the bud and neatly twisted shut at the top instead of leaving the ends sticking out, as in the Tobacco flower and Petunia.

The largest blossoms are found on the white MOON-FLOWER, and the largest seeds, too. These are the seeds that should have their outer skin nicked to help germination. It is an annual vine.

The HEAVENLY BLUES are not Moonflowers, since they do not open until morning. Their seeds are much smaller and have such thin skins that forty-eight hours of warmth and moisture brings them up. They will not grow until warm weather sets in, nor will they bloom in extreme heat. They seem to like best exactly the same temperatures that human beings do and demonstrate it by blooming happily all winter in our living rooms.

The CYPRESS-VINE and Cardinal Climber are good annual vines with small red blooms and divided foliage.

DODDER is a vicious weed that shows its family relationship only by its twining habit. It has no leaves, for leaves are food factories. It does not need them because it lives on stolen food! As soon as the first yellow tendril can reach to a neighboring plant, it develops little suckers that penetrate the skin of its host and steal its stores. On this borrowed food it grows rapidly and often forms a smothering mesh that destroys the plants which feed it. It even produces flower and seeds, and woe to a farmer who allows these seeds to mature and mix with the seed of his Clover, for it renders it unsalable.

The perennial Morning-Glories called BINDWEEDS are also foes of the farmer, though the name was lovingly given to them in India where their network of tough roots bound the sands and kept the sea from washing away the land.

In this country any Morning-Glory that spreads by root suckers should be destroyed at once. Some of them are more dangerous to farm crops than others but all are bad. No wonder that farmers even look with suspicion on the harmless annual Morning-Glories and Moonflowers.

The beautiful, pink, hardy double one listed in some catalogues as California-Rose (*Convolvulus japonicus* or *Calystegia*) should never be used except where its roots can be confined, as in window boxes.

MORNING-GLORY FAMILY
Convolvulaceae
(kon-vol-veu-lay'-see-eé)
Funnel flowers
Twisted buds

MOONFLOWER
Ipomoea noctiflora

MORNING-GLORY
Ipomoea purpurea
(y-poh-mee'-ah)

CYPRESS-VINE
Quamoclit pennata
(kwam'-oh-klit)

DODDER
Cuscuta glomerata
(kus-keu'-tah)

BINDWEED
Convolvulus arvensis
(kon-vol'-veu-lus)

The American-Born Phloxes

This is a native American family with so many lovely forms that a spirit of patriotism might well give it a place in every garden. Some have even suggested that it should have been our national flower.

Ranging from white through all the shades of red, and from lavender to purple, its colors are always clear and pleasing. The flowers, slender tubes flattened out at the top, are usually clustered in heads or spikes. The buds are rolled like those of the Morning-Glory.

The first one pictured is the odd sheep in the family, the Cup-and-Saucer-Vine, or PURPLEBELL COBAEA. Its purple bells, in their green saucers, dangle from a slender vine, which enjoys climbing your window screen by its tendril fingers, giving you a green lace shelter from the sun. Its odd seeds sprout best when set on edge.

TEXAS PLUME is a southern native that is a fairly hardy biennial in the North, making its tuft of cypress-like ground foliage one year and sending up its spike of flaming red flowers the next. It is sometimes called Standing Cypress.

The tall GARDEN PHLOX of our July perennial borders has been bred into its exquisite pinks, corals, and scarlets, from an original magenta color, to which most seedlings revert. To keep the color pure the propagation must be by root divisions or by stem or root cuttings. Phlox does not do well in a hot, dry location and in the Midwest should be given semishade and constant watering to prevent injury by the red spider. Don't let your choice plants go to seed or they may be smothered by their prolific, undesirable progeny.

The GILIAS are annuals easily grown from seed, and come in many bright colors.

Because of its bright pink blossoms PRAIRIE PHLOX is the brightest roadside flower in late May and early June. You may naturalize it in your garden if you can provide prairie conditions.

A similar plant, which prefers woodland to grassland, is BLUE PHLOX, Wild Sweet William, or Timber Phlox, with looser heads of bloom and a color range from white through many shades of lavender. It quickly makes itself at home among the shrubs in your yard, spreading by seed. For a pink and lavender border picture that will last for six weeks, it may be planted with a succession of various types of pink Tulips.

The dainty blue GREEK VALERIAN, or Jacobs Ladder, is a shade-loving native. Because of the shape of its flowers some people call it Bluebell. The fern-like leaves remain attractive all summer.

DRUMMOND PHLOX is the sun-loving, annual garden phlox. Its color range includes shades of soft yellow.

Rock gardens depend upon the MOSS PHLOXES for masses of color in white, lavender, purple, and pink. Their blooming period stretches over six weeks. The rest of the year the foliage remains mossy and tidy.

PHLOX FAMILY
Polemoniaceae
(pol-ee-moh-ni-ay'-see-ee)
Small tube flowers
Loose clusters

PURPLEBELL COBAEA
Cobaea scandens
(koh-bee'-ah)

TEXAS PLUME
Gilia rubra
(jil'-i-ah)

GARDEN PHLOX
Phlox paniculata
(flox)

BIRDSEYE GILIA
Gilia tricolor

PRAIRIE PHLOX
Phlox pilosa

BLUE PHLOX
Phlox divaricata

GREEK VALERIAN
Polemonium
(pol-ee-moh'-ni-um)

DRUMMOND PHLOX
Phlox Drummondii

MOSS PHLOX
Phlox subulata

83

Forget-Me-Nots and Other Blue Borages

This family is easily recognized because it wears its flower stem in a question mark. As the buds unfold, the spray gradually assumes a graceful horizontal position. With a very few exceptions the flowers are blue. The leaves are never divided.

Though belonging to the tube-flower group, some members of the family have tubes so short as to be almost unnoticeable. The flare above the tube is sometimes a smooth-edged bell, but usually it is divided into five lobes. The family has little food value but ranks high in romance and legend.

BUGLOSS is like a giant Forget-me-not, but it is banished to the background of our gardens because of its bristly leaves and stems. COMFREY, with bell-shaped flowers, also has coarse hairy foliage and is sometimes marked with white.

The family aristocrat is HELIOTROPE. Its subtle fragrance and soft lavender coloring make it a popular hothouse and bedding plant. It will bloom in August from seed sown outdoors in spring, but it will bloom much earlier from rooted cuttings.

VIRGINIA BLUEBELLS are one of our loveliest early flowers. Native to moist timberlands, their buds are first purple, then pink, and finally bells of softest caerulean blue. Rarely there is a white one. Their smooth, pale leaves soon die down and the fleshy roots remain dormant through the summer. Transplant them in the fall.

Although the preferred botanical name of SIBERIAN BUGLOSS is *Brunnera,* most of us have always known it as *Anchusa myosotidiflora* and gloried in being able to pro-

nounce such a tongue twister. *Myosotidiflora* means "with flowers like Forget-me-not," which describes the plant nicely. By any name, it is marvelous for rock gardens because its early blue blossoms are followed by foliage that remains beautiful all summer.

The hairy leaves and long leathery roots of PUCCOON are well adapted to its native hot prairies. The orange blooms are a surprise in this family. The roots give off an orange stain used as war paint by the Indians, as one might guess from its common names Redroot and Painter.

HOUND'S TONGUE looks like the *Anchusa* and is a useful blue annual. The seeds are beggar's-lice and selfsow to keep you supplied with plants year after year.

FORGET-ME-NOT has many types adapted to different uses. The biennial *Myosotis Alpestris* sown in late summer blooms with the next spring's Tulips. *Myosotis palustris,* which means "water-loving," is a true perennial, never without bloom after it starts in late May.

Forget-me-nots grow wild along every stream in Europe and the ancients explained its universal presence with the story of an immortal god who fell in love with a blue-eyed earth maiden. He begged the powers of heaven to make her immortal. They said they would do so if she would perform the seemingly impossible task of setting out Forget-me-nots in every corner of the world. Each evening he slipped down to help her, and other lovers, seeing their joy in the task, helped also. She must be immortal now, for Forget-me-nots are found even on the tops of mountains.

BORAGE FAMILY
Boraginaceae
(boh-raj-i-nay'-see-ee)
Question-mark spray
Usually blue

BUGLOSS
Anchusa italica
(an-keu'-sah)

COMFREY
Symphytum officinale
(sim'-fi-tum)

HELIOTROPE
Heliotropium
(hee-li-oh-troh'-pi-um)

BORAGE
Borago officinalis
(boh-ray'-go)

BLUEBELLS
Mertensia virginica
(mer-ten'-si-ah)

SIBERIAN BUGLOSS
Brunnera macrophylla
(broo-nee'-rah)

PUCCOON
Lithospermum
(lith-oh-spur'-mum)

HOUND'S TONGUE
Cynoglossum
(sin-oh-glos'-um)

FORGET-ME-NOT
Myosotis
(my-oh-soh'-tis)

85

Verbena and Water-Leaf

Of course you are acquainted with the annual VERBENAS. No garden is complete without their glowing crimsons and scarlets or their soft pinks and lavenders. Choose your colors to fit your taste. They will weave an oriental rug over your spent Tulip bed, or border your perennials, and often November finds them still blooming.

The flower head gives the effect of being flat, but close inspection shows that it is merely a condensed spike. The wild members of the family expand these spikes to great lengths, as in the BLUE VERVAIN, which starts blooming at the bottom in June and spends the rest of the summer getting to the top.

The individual flowers attempt to be two-sided like the Mints but have never quite succeeded in getting their mouths open. Otherwise you might mistake some of the wild ones for members of the Mint Family, for they have the same type of coarse, opposite leaves and even a tendency to have square stems.

LANTANAS are used for summer bedding of yellow, orange, and henna, or pink if you like pink. It is hard to realize that in the tropics they are the main source of firewood. Florists cut back the old plants in the fall and keep them dormant until spring, when their tender new growth makes easily rooted cuttings. They are difficult to grow from seeds and not dependable as to color. They are not hardy north of the citrus belt.

The perennial lavender WILD VERBENA of the Middle West makes a wonderful display in May and is a good plant for rock gardens, except that as the old wood dies in the middle of the clump and the new growth at the edge carries on, the plant gradually travels out of your garden unless renewed. A red-flowered form of this has been put on the market but has not proved to be as fully hardy.

A recently introduced annual species from South America is *Verbena bonariensis* (not illustrated), which grows to three feet and bears flower clusters much like those of Heliotrope, except for their lack of fragrance.

Verbena erinoides (not illustrated) is a hardy annual called Moss Verbena because of its finely cut foliage. The bloom is white or lavender.

Compare the Water-Leaf Family with the Borage Family on the preceding page and notice that they also have the question-mark way of arranging their pale blue, tubular blooms. Their leaves are quite different, however, usually being divided and often with odd "watered silk" splotches on them, suggesting the name Water-Leaf.

The two WATER-LEAFS look pretty when at home in damp woods, but you will rue the day you let them into your garden, for their stout roots are bad crowders. The lavender blossoms appear fluffy because of the protruding stamens.

The PHACELIAS and BABY BLUE-EYES, however, are innocent little blue annuals, which are beloved wild flowers in California. In the Middle West they must be started early in order to give them a chance to bloom before hot weather. The Baby Blue-eyes will selfsow in the shade.

VERBENA FAMILY
Verbenaceae
(ver-bee-nay'-see-ee)
Dense flower heads
Rough, notched leaves

WATER-LEAF FAMILY
Hydrophyllaceae
(hy-droh-fil-lay'-see-ee)
Bell-shaped flowers
Cut foliage

BLUE VERVAIN
Verbena hastata
(ver-bee'-nah)

GARDEN VERBENA
Verbena

VIRGINIA WATER-LEAF
Hydrophyllum virginianum

PHACELIA
Phacelia
(fa-see'-li-ah)

LANTANA
Lantana Camara
(lan-tah'-nah)

WATER-LEAF
Hydrophyllum appendiculatum
(hy-droh-fill'-um)

BABY BLUE-EYES
Nemophila
(ne-mof'-i-lah)

87

Flavorsome Mints

When you find a plant with a square stem, strong smell, opposite leaves, and two-lipped flowers, you may be quite sure that it is a Mint. The flowers open a wide mouth, the upper lip of which is usually two-lobed and smaller than the three-lobed lower one. These flowers cluster in the axils of the leaves or form spikes at the tip of the spray.

The family is friendly and helpful and seems to love the society of mankind, for around every dooryard may be found plants of MOTHERWORT and CATNIP, which furnish tonic for man and beast. Many are grown in little herb gardens. Peppermint and Spearmint are grown commercially in the rich swamplands of Michigan.

SPEARMINT, so called because of its slender flower spike, is the source of Mint leaves for juleps and lamb sauce, and its distilled oil furnishes flavor for chewing gum. To ensure always having fresh leaves, cut back different plants in turn.

GARDEN SAGE is a perennial with lavender flowers pretty enough for bouquets but valued mostly because of the flavor that its dried leaves add to meats. Every garden should have a few plants so that you may be sure of a fresh product when needed.

PENNYROYAL is supposed to ward off mosquitoes, either when grown in their haunts or when its oil is used as a lotion for rubbing on the hands and face.

HENBIT, with rosy flowers, is so attractive in early spring that you may be tempted to bring it into your garden, but if you do you will have a long fight to get rid of it. It has a bad habit of producing seeds so late in the fall and so early in the spring that we forget to watch for them.

As a bad spreader it is more than equaled by GROUND IVY, an innocent-looking little pest with round leaves and lavender flowers that thinks nothing of killing a Blue Grass lawn. The only place it should be used is in a barren spot that will grow nothing else.

Ground Ivy has a respectable and beautiful sister, *Nepeta glechoma varigata,* with green foliage vividly splashed with white and touches of pink. Barely winter-hardy out of doors, it makes a good hanging-basket vine for the window, or a ground cover for Geraniums or *Coleus.*

SELF-HEAL and CARPET BUGLE are somewhat of the same nature as Ground Ivy but their ample flowers are in spikes large enough to add real beauty to shady spots and they never travel far enough into the sunshine to compete with garden flowers. Possibly in climates cooler than the Middle West they will need watching.

In your herb garden you may also use from this family Balm, Basil, Clary, Hoarhound, Hyssop, Marjoram, Rosemary, and Summer Savory. These are called leaf herbs and are harvested just before their blossoms open, for that is the time when they are most aromatic. The cut stems are hung in an airy place to cure. When fully dried the unbroken leaves are saved for teas, and the fragments are powdered and stored in closed jars until needed for flavoring meats.

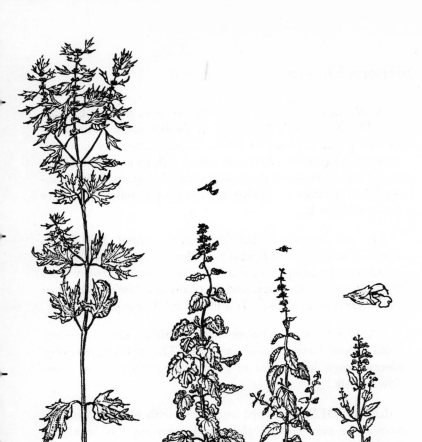

MINT FAMILY
Labiatae
(lay-bi-ay'-tee)
Square stems
Fragrant foliage

CATNIP
Nepeta Cataria
(nep'-e-ta)

SAGE
Salvia officinalis

HENBIT
Lamium
(lay'-mi-um)

CARPET BUGLE
Ajuga reptans
(a-jeu'-gah)

MOTHERWORT
Leonurus Cardiaca
(le-o-new'-rus)

SPEARMINT
Mentha spicata
(men'-thah)

PRAIRIE PENNYROYAL
Hedeoma hispida
(he-dee-o'-ma)

SELF-HEAL
Prunella
(proo-nel'-ah)

GROUND IVY
Nepeta hederacea

89

Mints with Conspicuous Flowers

On the preceding page were shown mostly the useful Mints and the weedy ones. Here we have the ornamental ones. Most of the Salvias are very showy. The tall perennial AZURE SAGE has been brought from the roadside to serve with Delphiniums in furnishing spires of blue in our borders.

The Monardas bunch their tubes at the top to attract bees. They are native American wild flowers. The red one, OSWEGO-TEA, loves moisture and semishade and will be glad to brighten a dark corner in your yard. The lavender one, Horse Balm, is at home along sunny roadsides.

FALSE DRAGON-HEAD is a September-blooming perennial that defies our criticism of its magenta color with a good-natured readiness to bloom through all hardship. There is also a white form. It has no aroma, but its square stem and lipped flower proclaim it a Mint. Its habit of wearing its blooms on whichever side of the stem they are pushed has given it the name of Obedient Plant. It has many other folk names. Put it back among your shrubbery and forget about it until needed.

The annual SCARLET SAGE, or Red Salvia, is one of the very reddest flowers known, because even its calyx and flower stem are red. This intense color has to be handled with caution or we tire of it. Give it a dark green background removed from flowers in other shades of red. Although fond of sunshine it will do surprisingly well on the north side of the house, and young plants potted in the fall will bloom indoors all winter.

An old-fashioned mint with several names is MOLUCCA-BALM, Old-Maid's-Nightcap, or Shell-Flower. The shells are very much enlarged green calyxes. The tiny lavender blossom is far inside. After the leaves fall, these stiff shells remain and when dried make interesting bouquets. It is an annual but selfsows so readily that once you have it you are never without it.

Are you surprised that the many-colored FOLIAGE PLANT is a Mint? Or had you already noticed its square stems and two-lipped flowers? It too is easily grown from seeds as well as cuttings, and its colors are more brilliant in the shade than in the sun. It is useful as a house plant.

LAMBS-EARS has leaves so like a rabbit's ears that every child should have a plant as a pet! The brilliant magenta blooms, each in a calyx of gray velvet, make an arresting flower stalk.

LAVENDER is a word associated with old lace and romance. It comes from the word meaning "to lave," or "wash," because from time immemorial its sprigs have been placed with freshly laundered linens. Its fragrance is so elusive that one never tires of it, and it is a garden treasure, especially in hot climates, where its culture is difficult.

THYME is a fragrant-leaved trailer whose varied types are used in rock gardens, as ground covers, and as culinary herbs. A good nursery catalogue is the best place to study them in detail.

OSWEGO-TEA
Monarda didyma
(moh-nahr'-dah)

SCARLET SAGE
Salvia splendens

FOLIAGE PLANT
Coleus
(koh'-lee-us)

LAVENDER
Lavandula
(lah-van'-deu-lah)

AZURE SAGE
Salvia azurea
(sal'-vi-ah)

FALSE DRAGON-HEAD
Physostegia
(fy-soh-stee'-ji-ah)

MOLUCCA-BALM
Molucella laevis
(mol-eu-sel'-ah)

LAMBS-EARS
Stachys lanata
(stay'-kiss)

MOTHER-OF-THYME
Thymus Serpyllum
(ty'-mus)

Nightshades, Some Edible, Some Poisonous

This is one of the truly great plant families. It has developed in so many forms that it could take care of the world alone, if need be. An average dinner might easily use its Potatoes, Eggplant, Peppers, and Tomatoes, with Petunias, Schizanthus, or Salpiglossis for the centerpiece. There would even be Tobacco for the after-dinner smoke! The meal might be cooked with alcohol distilled from the Potato and there would be half a dozen drugs to choose from should you become ill. Like every large family it has a few black sheep in the form of prickly weeds and poisonous fruits.

The typical flower of the family is the flat five-pointed star, with the anthers making a yellow tent around the pistil. Most of the plants are sprawly, with the flowers set in the axils of their alternate leaves.

Of course the POTATOES are its big gift. They originated in South America rather than in Ireland! When first introduced into Europe they were no larger than Walnuts, but they have been gradually improved until they now feed a greater proportion of the earth's inhabitants than any other crop except Rice. When Sir Walter Raleigh learned from the Indians how to use them, he wrote home enthusiastically that they were "white as flour and sweet as a nut."

The little element of poison that lurks in the Nightshade Family develops in the green of sunburned Potatoes, and it is best not to eat them. Potato seeds are poisonous also, and that is probably what made people afraid to eat TOMATOES for many years after their introduction.

BITTER NIGHTSHADE, or Bittersweet Nightshade, the climbing variety, bears lavender flowers and beautiful red berries, which are listed as poisonous to people but not to birds. It attracts potato bugs to the premises.

BLACK NIGHTSHADE is often referred to as Deadly Nightshade or Poison Berry, and while there is no record that death has been caused by eating its berries, there is no question but that they may cause violent nausea, especially when a bit green. Since the plant is an annual, it is easily eradicated. The drug belladonna is extracted from the roots of the true Deadly Nightshade, *Atropa Belladonna*.

CHINESE LANTERN PLANT is a Ground Cherry with inflated pods of vivid orange-scarlet. These pods when dried are much used for winter bouquets. The plants will grow in semishade but are best kept out of the garden because of their spreading roots. In nearly every pod will be found a hole, through which has escaped a little worm, hatched from an egg laid in the bloom.

JERUSALEM-CHERRY makes a cheery Christmas plant easily grown at home. Handle it just as you would Tomato plants, potting them in August. In the house, keep it away from drafts. It is said that they fruit more heavily when visited by bees. When it is through fruiting, cut it back severely and place it in a cool north window. Keep all new growth pinched back. Repot with fresh soil in the spring, and sink the pot in a sunny spot for the summer.

NIGHTSHADE FAMILY
Solanaceae
(sol-ah-nay′-see-ee)
Star-shaped flower
Strong scent

TOMATO
Lycopersicon esculentum
(ly-koh-pur′-si-kon)

BLACK NIGHTSHADE
Solanum nigrum

JERUSALEM-CHERRY
Solanum Pseudo-Capsicum

TTER NIGHTSHADE
Solanum Dulcamara
(soh-lah′-mum)

POTATO
Solanum tuberosum

CHINESE LANTERN PLANT
Physalis Alkekengi
(fis′-ah-lis)

Handsome Cousins of the Earthy Potato

This wonderful family seems to have considered every possible need of the human race. Besides giving us bright flowers for daytime, it has provided white ones for night.

The great white discs of ANGELS TRUMPET are sometimes called Moonflower, but that name properly belongs to a night-blooming relative of the Morning-Glory. Angels Trumpet is related to the foul-smelling Jimson Weed, which springs up in rich wastelands. The seeds of this weed contain a strong drug that was formerly much used to produce fantastic dreams. It was named by the colonists at Jamestown, Virginia, where it was discovered.

The starry blooms of the JASMINE TOBACCO open at twilight and send out a heavy fragrance. It is an annual. Commercial Tobacco is a form of this plant.

Tree Tobacco (*Nicotiana glauca,* not illustrated) is a spectacular background annual for large gardens. It will grow to twelve feet, with a cluster of yellow tubular flowers at the top.

BUTTERFLY-FLOWER has fragile blossoms that are like Orchids in their odd colorings and elfin shapes. It is an annual easily grown from seeds and at its best in the greenhouse. It needs cool weather and moist air to thrive out of doors. The best plan is to start it early and make frequent plantings. Some of the plants will surely strike a cool spell.

The SALPIGLOSSIS is very beautiful, with gold lace covering its cloak of rich purple, maroon, or crimson velvet. It is as easily grown as Petunias. We should use it more.

BROWALLIAS in their dwarf form give a supply of blue in the annual garden all through the summer, sending up new growth from the base each time that the old is cut back. The large form is a splendid window bloomer but a failure in the garden.

PETUNIAS are a garden stand-by. Even their volunteer magenta seedlings are better than nothing, but you will get a real thrill from the beautiful new shades of rose and blue. The white ones add romance when reflected in your pool. They are the best window-box flower, but for a good effect the same color should be used at all windows. You will like white best for red-brick houses.

Pot up a few young plants in the fall and they will fill your windows with bloom in the late winter. I know one woman of very limited means who satisfies her craving for beauty and perfection by buying each year a few seeds of the very finest of the new fringed Petunias. She gives them such loving care that no millionaire flower-fancier has finer blooms than she.

The CUP-FLOWERS have the same family form as do the Potato blossoms, but their foliage is very much like that of Flax. They are tender perennials, blooming in August from spring-sown seeds and easily carried over in a cool, light cellar to bloom in your window in April. Later they may grace your garden. The lavender one, *hippomanica,* is considered the best and if you do not already have it you will surely thank us for the introduction.

GELS TRUMPET
atura fastuosa alba
(dah-teu′-rah)

JASMINE TOBACCO
Nicotiana alata
(ni-koh-shi-ay′-nah)

BUTTERFLY-FLOWER
Schizanthus pinnatus
(sky-zan′-thus)

SALPIGLOSSIS
Salpiglossis
(sal-pi-glos′-is)

BROWALLIA
Browallia demissa
(broh-wal′-i-ah)

PETUNIA
Petunia
(pe-teu′-ni-ah)

CUP-FLOWER
Nierembergia
(nee-rem-ber′-ji-ah)

Flowers with Jaws

Aren't these flowers oddly shaped? You'd think some of them really were designed from fantastic animals. Throats are swollen. Jaws move up and down, or hang hungrily open. Occasionally the jaws are absent and the tube opens smoothly into irregular scallops.

This family contains many of our choicest garden flowers. The blossoms are usually arranged in spires, and the leaves are usually opposite.

TRUE FOXGLOVE gives us the valuable heart sedative digitalis. This narcotic quality makes the roots poisonous. But it is an aristocrat in our gardens because of its colorful purple, pink, or lavender flowers. Since it is a biennial, seed must be planted each year. Try it with ferns in a shaded corner.

The perennial YELLOW FOXGLOVE, with bells of soft yellow speckled with brown, is not so spectacular but is a very useful garden subject. If not allowed to make seeds it has at least three bloom periods throughout the summer.

A dozen common names are given to the tallest and largest-flowered wild Pentstemon. Called SHELL-LEAF PENT-STEMON because of its stiff gray shell-shaped leaves, it is also known as Bluff-Bluebells because of its love for the Missouri River bluffs. Although it is a true perennial on poor, clay soil it is apt to be only a biennial in our gardens. It is well worth the task of resowing and often selfsows.

Many more species of native Pentstemon are proving such good garden subjects that their collection is becoming a hobby. They include varieties as blue as Gentians and much easier to grow.

The wild Snapdragons are scornfully called Toadflax, or Butter and Eggs. They are always in shades of yellow and orange and are bad spreaders. However, the one called MACEDONIAN TOADFLAX is so beautiful, both as a cut flower and for its gray foliage, that you might well give it a life lease on some difficult corner of your garden.

TORREY PENTSTEMON with its graceful sprays of dangling firecrackers in red or pink should be in every perennial border. It is sometimes listed under the name of Chelone, for you will notice that it has a tendency to the same turtle-head shape as the true Chelone TURTLE-HEAD, a much more weedy plant used only in the wild garden.

SNAPDRAGONS are one of the family aristocrats. They come in such exquisite colors and are so much grown in hothouses for winter cut flowers that, even though grown in our annual gardens, they have an exotic air. Be sure to buy seeds of rustproof varieties.

TOADFLAX, or Fairy Bouquet, is an excellent little annual. Its daintily colored, fantastic blooms seem to dance over the plant. The many varieties of dwarf *Linaria* make easy window plants for winter if seeds are sown in pots in August and are kept cool.

KENILWORTH-IVY surely has a Snapdragon blossom, but the botanists tell us to call it *Cymbalaria*. It is a fine house plant vine.

FIGWORT FAMILY
Scrophulariaceae
(skrof-eu-lay-ri-ay'-see-ee)
Swollen tube flowers
Curious mouths

SHELL-LEAF PENTSTEMON
Pentstemon grandiflorus
(pent-stee'-mon)

TORREY PENTSTEMON
Pentstemon barbatus Torreyi

YELLOW FOXGLOVE
Digitalis ambigua

TOADFLAX
Linaria maroccana

FOXGLOVE
Digitalis purpurea
(dij-i-tay'-lis)

MACEDONIAN TOADFLAX
Linaria macedonica
(ly-nay'-ri-ah)

TURTLE-HEAD
Chelone lyoni
(ke-loh'-nee)

SNAPDRAGON
Antirrhinum
(an-ti-ry'-num)

KENILWORTH-IVY
Cymbalaria muralis
(sim-ba-lay'-ri-a)

97

More Odd Faces

These plants are more members of the Figwort Family. The wild MULLEINS are such persistent weeds in waste places that we are apt to lose sight of the beauty of their gray-velvet foliage and spikes of yellow flowers. However, experts in flower arrangement have discovered them and use the gray rosettes for accent among evergreen material. The nap on the leaves is really a mass of prickly points to discourage browsing animals. The plants form a thick rosette of leaves the first year and send up their tall flower stalks the second. For several months blooms open each morning and fall off when the sun gets hot.

There are improved forms in various shades of yellow, as well as a dwarf type with lavender, pink, and white flowers that bloom at Iris time.

The name Veronica means "very image" because the flowers of some of them seem to show a face. Perhaps your imagination can find it in the last picture on the page. Under the name Speedwell they furnish some of the best blue flowers for the garden and sometimes have white and lavender varieties. The tall wild white one illustrated is the CULVER'S PHYSIC of our autumn woods.

CALCEOLARIA comes from a word meaning "slipper," and each of its colorful blooms is made up of two slippers, a large one and a very small one. Ladies' Pocketbook is another common name. Usually they are spoken of with a respect that demands their scientific name, for their growing requires experts, even in the greenhouse. If you should receive a potted one as a gift, keep it in a cool room. They can stand winter sun but after March should be kept in a north window. They are tender perennials and if you have "green fingers" you may possibly get one to bloom a second time. You may also try raising it from seed.

The MASK-FLOWERS are delicate annuals that are worth experimenting with for novelty, but their blooming period is short. The brilliant flowers are bright yellow, orange, and red. They are difficult to grow where summers are hot, but in cool climates they make excellent and colorful bedding plants. They are also interesting greenhouse subjects.

The woolly native WOOD BETONY, or Lousewort, looks very much like the Mints but has a round stem. Its flowers are yellow with crimson. Place it among your ferns.

TORENIA, an annual, is a real blessing for the shaded garden after midsummer, for it gives a profusion of lavender flowers touched with orange and deep purple, which from a distance look almost exactly like Pansies. They like the same conditions as Begonias. The common name Wishbone Flower comes from the wishbone-shaped arrangement of the stamens.

For study of the dwarf VERONICAS, refer to some recent catalogue of rock garden plants, for they are being constantly hybridized and improved. Their vivid blues and soft lavenders are beautiful among the rocks.

Others of this family but not illustrated are *Castilleja* (Painted Cup), *Collinsia,* and *Mimulus* (Monkey Flower).

MULLEIN
Verbascum Thapsus
(ver-bas′-kum)

CULVER'S PHYSIC
Veronica virginica
(ve-ron′-i-kah)

CALCEOLARIA
Calceolaria
(kal-se-oh-lay′-ri-ah)

MASK-FLOWER
Alonsoa
(al-on-soh′-ah)

WOOD BETONY
Pedicularis
(pe-dik-eu-lay′-ris)

TORENIA
Torenia
(toh-ree′-ni-ah)

MASK-FLOWER
Nemesia
(ne-mee′-si-ah)

LOW VERONICA
Veronica

Window Garden Favorites and the Lobelias

From the Acanthus Family we show two lovely orphans, far away from their tropical relatives, but decidedly worthy of being adopted into any garden. The pleading dark eyes of BLACK-EYED CLOCKVINE will call to you from some greenhouse bench, for it needs an early start in order to cover your trellis with yellow, orange, or creamy blooms before midsummer. It is one of the few vines that blooms well in a north exposure and makes a fine trailer for a window box.

Its sister, HAIRY RUELLIA, is made of sterner stuff and delights in the hottest and driest roadside, where its petunia-like flowers of soft lavender defy the hot winds of July and August. It is often called Wild-Petunia. Its leaves and stems account for its name "hairy." You will like it in your perennial border, where it will show its gratitude by a generous gift of seedlings. Try a bank of it at the base of your Tiger Lilies.

Also of this family, but not illustrated are *Strobilanthes* (Conehead or Royal Purple Plant) and *Beloperone* (Shrimp-plant).

From the hot, moist jungles of the tropics comes the Gesneria Family, with thick-leaved, hairy plants and gorgeous flowers. Since they all prefer shade and dislike water on their leaves, it is probable that their favorite native locations were on mossy banks protected from both sun and wind by heavy overhead foliage.

Both GLOXINIAS and AFRICAN VIOLETS may be started by inserting the stems of leaves in sand or water, but they also come easily from seed, which will produce blooming plants in August if sown in February—if you can reproduce jungle climate! Also of this family but not illustrated is *Achimenes*.

The LOBELIAS are much like the Bellflowers in leaf and seed habits, but they differ in having their blossom tube split into ragged streamers, the two top ones usually smaller than the three lower ones. Their stamens have grown together into a tube around the pistil. This tube is so long that only the hummingbirds have a tongue long enough to reach the honey at its base.

The vivid red CARDINAL-FLOWER is very showy against the dark foliage of the moist, shady places it loves.

The native BLUE LOBELIA, which the Indians thought was a remedy for syphilis, is bright blue. Its bloom suggests that of the Mints, but its stem is not square. In late summer it decorates moist lowlands or perhaps your garden.

The commonest wild Lobelia is INDIAN TOBACCO, which we scarcely notice when its small, pale blue flowers are open. But in the fall its orange seed balls, which are quite poisonous, make it conspicuous.

The little annual EDGING LOBELIA is much used for borders, baskets, and porch boxes. Like its tall sisters it thrives best in cool climates.

ACANTHUS FAMILY
Acanthaceae
(a-kan-thay′-see-ee)

GESNERIA FAMILY
Gesneriaceae
(jes-ner-i-ay′-see-ee)
Hairy leaves
Tube flowers

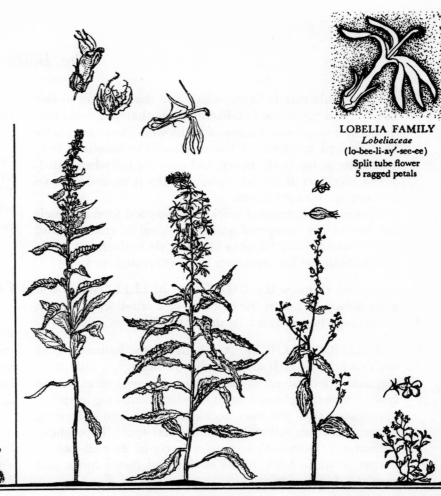

LOBELIA FAMILY
Lobeliaceae
(lo-bee-li-ay′-see-ee)
Split tube flower
5 ragged petals

RUELLIA
Ruellia ciliosa
(roo-el′-i-ah)

AFRICAN VIOLET
Saintpaulia
(saynt-pau′-li-ah)

CARDINAL-FLOWER
Lobelia cardinalis
(loh-bee′-li-ah)

EDGING LOBELIA
Lobelia Erinus

ACK-EYED CLOCKVINE
Thunbergia alata
(thun-bur′-ji-ah)

GLOXINIA
Sinningia
(si-nin′-ji-ah)

BLUE LOBELIA
Lobelia syphilitica

INDIAN TOBACCO
Lobelia inflata

101

The Bellflowers

Campanula means "little bells," and the blossoms in this family certainly are so bell-like in shape that you could easily guess their common name of Bellflower. They are usually blue, though sometimes white or pink. The corolla is five-lobed, sits on top of the ovary, and does not fall when faded. A few members of the family have milky juice and all have alternately arranged leaves.

This family responded quickly to the good food and mellow soil of our cultivated gardens, taking on enlarged and double forms. Gray's *Botany* lists only six natives, but many a seed catalogue lists twenty or more cultivated ones.

In cool climates the CHIMNEY BELLFLOWER will grow almost as tall as the chimney of a one-story house. In hot regions, however, it fails almost totally.

BALLOON-FLOWER (the buds are the balloons) does not mind the heat. It asks only good drainage, a little staking, and a long sleep in the spring. It is wise to mark the space where it is planted, for it is so late in making its spring appearance that you may accidentally dig into it or even attempt to plant something else in that spot! Throughout midsummer Balloon-Flower gives freely of its cool-looking purple or white bells. It has double and dwarf forms and grows wild in the Orient.

CANTERBURY BELLS have the largest and most fantastic blooms in the family. Plant the double form *calycanthema* and along with its true double progeny, cup within cup, you will also get plenty that are merely cup and saucer and some that are cup alone. They are biennial in habit, and

winter better if wilted a little in the fall by disturbing the roots.

FALSE RAMPION'S scientific name *rapunculoides* means "little turnip," so we should not be surprised to hear that the thick root stalks of its wild variety are eaten as salads in Europe. It will quickly spread over your garden whether you wish it to do so or not, and will furnish lavender bells to arrange with your pink Roses.

An exquisite border plant is the PEACHLEAF BELLFLOWER, obviously so called because the leaves resemble Peach leaves.

Two rather weedy, though interesting natives, are TALL BELLFLOWER and VENUS' LOOKING-GLASS. A more cosmopolitan wildling is HAREBELL, found in all parts of the world and famous particularly as the Bluebells of Scotland. *Rotundifolia* means "round leaves," referring in this case to the basal ones.

DANE'S-BLOOD is named *glomerata* from its habit of holding its purple bells upright in a "glome." It is one of the showiest of low-growing garden perennials and is as easy to grow as it is attractive. The leaves are hairy.

Our best perennial edging plant is CARPATHIAN BELLFLOWER. Perfectly hardy and with good foliage, it bears its blue or white flowers in profusion from May until frost. Also of this family but not illustrated is *Campanula isophylla* (Star-of-Bethlehem).

BELLFLOWER FAMILY
Campanulaceae
(kam-pan-eu-lay'-see-ee)
5-petaled bell
Usually blue

HIMNEY BELLFLOWER
Campanula pyrimidalis

CANTERBURY BELLS
Campanula Medium
(kam-pan'-eu-lah)

PEACHLEAF BELLFLOWER
Campanula persicifolia

HAREBELL
Campanula rotundifolia

DANE'S-BLOOD
Campanula glomerata

BALLOON FLOWER
Platycodon
(plat-i-koh'-don)

FALSE RAMPION
Campanula rapunculoides

TALL BELLFLOWER
Campanula americana

VENUS'
LOOKING-GLASS
Specularia Speculum
(spek-eu-lay'-ri-ah)

CARPATHIAN
BELLFLOWER
Campanula carpatica

103

Some Interesting Strays

This is a page of "lone wolf" families, which have few representatives in our country. The fragrant VALERIAN, or Garden Heliotrope, which is found in all old gardens, is from the Mediterranean regions, where its family is the source of supply of the drug valerian. The flowers are pinkish-lavender or white and are fragrant. The leaves are fern-like. Its height and airy appearance make it an excellent background plant. It is a perennial and easily divided.

TEASEL was brought into this country to supply weavers with hooked burs to tease up the nap on cloth. It has spread through eastern meadows, where it is a mean weed. Its scientific name refers to its dippers, water-holding basins at the base of each leaf.

The SCABIOSA, or Pincushion-Flower, is another member of the Teasel Family. The pins are the pistils and stamens, which project from the cushion-like center. We show the perennial form. In the annual form the heads are rounded on top and much more fluffy. The colors are soft pink, lavender, and white.

The SPIDER-FLOWER is so named because of the spider-leg effect of its long slender seed pods. It is of the same family as Capers, which are used for Caper sauce. The bottled Capers are the peppery flower buds of an oriental relative, but the seed pods of our native would give the same taste, and possibly a fortune awaits the person who introduces them. Thousands of acres of waste land in Nebraska and Colorado are covered with its pink bloom, giving it the name of Rocky Mountain Bee Plant. Still another name is Electric Light Plant. It shows close relationship to the Mustards by its four-petaled blooms, as well as by its taste. It is a splendid annual background plant.

The fragrance arising when you brush your hand across leaf, flower, or seed of the GAS-PLANT discloses its relation to the Lemon and Orange. So heavily is it stored with this citrus oil that on hot days a gas rises that will give a flash of flame if touched with a match. Hence the name.

It is an old, old garden plant, called Dittany in England. Many like its white variety better than the lavender-pink ones. Its hard-shelled seeds must lie over winter in the ground before they will sprout, and it takes years for them to reach blooming size. Decide carefully where you want them permanently, for they will outlive you!

The MAY APPLE is brother to the Barberry. The flowers, and later the pale green, tasteless apples, hide under large green umbrellas.

Sweet, modest MIGNONETTE when seen through a microscope dons a less sober frock of exquisite texture and beauty. Her name *reseda* means "to calm" and her subtle fragrance has that effect upon everyone. This beloved plant is found not only in the annual garden but in greenhouse and cottage window. Alfred Hottes, the garden authority who knows and loves all flowers, has chosen Mignonette as his favorite.

TEASEL
Dipsacus
(dip'-sah-kus)

SPIDER-FLOWER
Cleome spinosa
(klee-oh'-me)

MAY APPLE
Podophyllum peltatum
(pod-oh-fil'-um)

CAUCASIAN SCABIOSA
Scabiosa caucasica
(skay-bi-oh'-sah)

GAS-PLANT
Dictamnus
(dik-tam'-nus)

VALERIAN
Valeriana officinalis
(vah-lee-ri-ay'-nah)

MIGNONETTE
Reseda odorata
(re-see'-dah)

Cooperative Flowers

Botanists say that plants reach their highest development in the flowers called *Compositae*. Most of them wear "frills around the neck in just the Daisy's fashion!"

Very skillfully they arrange hundreds of simply garbed workers called disk flowers in the center of a comfortable receptacle. Around the edge they place a gay border of ray flowers, which attract the necessary bees and butterflies. Each disk flower is given the materials to produce a seed, and it all works out as efficiently as the production line in an automobile factory. (See page 3.) Since no two varieties agree as to shop methods and each one is eager to turn out the best-selling model, their summer style show is of never-ending interest to nature lovers.

We might call this first page of cooperative flowers the Beggar-Tick Family. Its hobby is the making of very thin seeds, closely packed and with their top end sharply pronged and hooked, ready to catch a ride on passing animals or on your clothing.

DAHLIAS, like other garden members of this group, have left off the hooks, since they have discovered that for some reason we lug their seeds around voluntarily. They grow easily from seed and bloom the first year if planted early. But the Dahlia doesn't need to make seeds at all if it prefers to produce ray flowers (double forms) only, for then we propagate it by tubers carried over winter in the cellar.

Dwarf Dahlias are fine fillers for the summer border, and their blossoms make daintily aristocratic arrangements. The tall types are spectacular. Stories of "my largest Dahlia" are as wild as fish stories! Double or single, each is more beautiful than the last. To produce an extra large flower, all side buds on that stalk are removed.

Did you realize that COSMOS was so much like Dahlia? The pictures show the resemblance in their branching habits. The colors run to the same lovely lavenders, pinks, and purple, and inside the heads you will find the same sort of thin, brown seeds. It is an easy annual, useful for cutting or to add height at the back of a border.

The recently introduced ORANGE FLARE Cosmos is a surprising color until you remember its wild cousins of the pasture. There are early varieties. Be sure to try it for hot weather bloom.

BEGGAR-TICKS are the yellow of our August meadows and the bane of our autumn hikes. There are many different sorts, some quite beautiful and others all business.

COREOPSIS is a splendid garden perennial, and if its flowers are kept picked, it will bloom all summer. It is particularly effective in the July garden when massed with the blue Balloon Flower. As a cut flower it is the best yellow "Daisy." It will selfsow and keep you well supplied with young plants.

Our gardens would miss the Beggar-Tick Family, but you will discover many assorted and questionable relatives hanging on whenever you take a woodland walk!

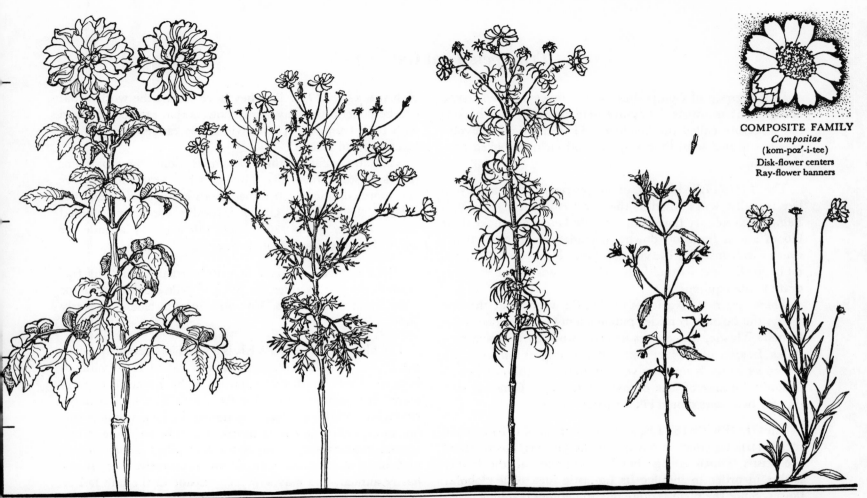

COMPOSITE FAMILY
Compositae
(kom-poz'-i-tee)
Disk-flower centers
Ray-flower banners

DAHLIA
Dahlia
(dal'-yah)

Var. ORANGE FLARE
Cosmos

COSMOS
Cosmos bipinnatus
(koz'-mos)

BEGGAR-TICKS
Bidens comosa
(by'-denz)

COREOPSIS
Coreopsis lanceolata
(koh-ree-op'-sis)

Trumpets That Get Together

In this group of Composites the ray flowers have become conspicuous trumpets. They are held together in a basket-like structure called the involucre. These particular involucres are armed with thorny spikes and vicious hooked bristles.

The THISTLE, because of its pugnacity and ability to live frugally, was chosen as the floral emblem of Scotland. Being often solitary flowers in a barren land, they make their bloom into a fragrant, downy, lavender couch and attract every weary insect in the vicinity. Since it may be a long distance to the next foothold, the Thistle seeds are given elaborate flying equipment.

There are many varieties of Thistle weeds, but the one which the farmers consider public enemy number one is the Canada Thistle, which does its dirty work by creeping root stalks. In spite of the fact that in many states it is against the law to let its seeds ripen on your premises, it still marches on defiantly because of lack of law enforcement. Constant cutting for two years should kill it by starvation.

The GLOBE THISTLE, whose clusters of blue balls make such a striking effect in our perennial gardens, has retained the bristly Thistle foliage but has sacrificed all the family basket in order to indulge its fantastic idea of a globular flower. Since the plant is quite tall, sometimes reaching seven feet, and the foliage is coarse as well as prickly, use it for a background effect or among shrubs.

The Centaureas have dispensed with prickles but retain their overlapping baskets, which give them the popular name of BASKET FLOWER. They have shown the world what can be done in the way of ray flowers that attract attention with their trumpets. Their vivid colors range through blue, lavender, and yellow.

Some are annual, others perennial. Some have blossoms that look suspiciously like Thistles, while others have fewer and more conspicuous trumpets worn in a fringe around the edge of their basket. Under favorable conditions, annual Basket Flower grows several feet tall and has lavender or white blossoms often five inches across.

SWEET SULTAN is a favorite garden annual, its fragrant flowers of lavender, purple, and yellow being useful for early summer bouquets. Volunteer plants bloom by early June.

The blue CORN-FLOWER is a weed in Europe, but cannot be very troublesome, since it was called Kaiserblumen because it was the favorite flower of the Emperor of Germany. It is incorrect to call it Bachelor's Button, that name belonging rightly to Globe Amaranth. In its many new colors and double and dwarf forms, it is most welcome in our annual gardens and is one of the best fillers among perennials or in waste corners. It selfsows pleasantly. Since it is a hardy annual, you may sow seed outside in the late fall or very early spring.

MOUNTAIN BLUET, or Perennial Corn-Flower, does indeed look like a Corn-Flower that has suddenly grown sturdier. It is fine for the front of the perennial border, where its blue flowers are interesting rather than showy.

THISTLE
Cirsium
(sir'-si-um)

GLOBE THISTLE
Echinops sphaerocephalus
(ek'-i-nops)

BASKET FLOWER
Centaurea americana

SWEET SULTAN
Centaurea imperialis

CORN-FLOWER
Centaurea Cyanus
(sen-tau-ree'-ah)

MOUNTAIN BLUET
Centaurea montana

Asters

The plants on this page are mostly Asters, though you may have called them Daisies, because there is a tendency to give that name to every flower with a frill of slender petals.

There are hundreds of varieties of GOLDEN-ROD, but all are easily recognized by their habit of arranging their yellow flowers in little tufts along the stem, like rows of duplicate houses in a factory village. We will have to call them apartment houses though, for each tuft contains its group of disk flowers surrounded by a few inconspicuous ray flowers.

MARE'S-TAIL, the Canada Fleabane, has masses of tiny little Daisies at the tip of a stalk, and like the larger, white-flowered DAISY FLEABANE is a widespread noxious weed hated by farmers. Do not be tempted to use Daisy Fleabane in your garden, for it has spreading habits. Another aster-like flower also known as Fleabane is the highly desirable lavender *Erigeron* (not illustrated).

The white or pink BOLTONIA of our gardens is also a weed in wet locations but not a bad spreader. Because it lops over when it has grown to its full height of five feet, it is a good plan to nip it back when about a foot tall. Some people even use it for garden hedges.

We had so long taken for granted the beauty of our native Hardy Asters that it was a surprise to have them taken up with great enthusiasm in Europe, where they have been much hybridized. We have pictured only two, showing extreme differences in leaf characteristics—the NEW ENGLAND ASTERS and LINDLEYS. There are innumerable in-between kinds. The Europeans have developed many new dwarf types for use in the war cemeteries, and we have found them useful for the gap that precedes the opening of the Chrysanthemum season.

The CHINA ASTER is a beautiful annual that is easily victimized by so many pests that we almost gave up trying to grow it. Now, however, we have learned that success follows if we use seed of wilt-resistant varieties and plant them in a new place each year. It will endure half-shade.

It is distinctly a town flower, for if grown near meadows the leaf hoppers bring in virus diseases from the wild Asters. And if cornfields are close, the ants will carry in the gray-green corn-root aphis. A generous application of tobacco or a good strong insecticide in the seed row when planting is a good preventive measure. The single and anemone-flowered China Asters are not subject to so many pests as the double ones and make good selfsowing subjects for the hardy border.

The ROCK ASTERS that bloom in our rock gardens in May are another species, with flowers not clustered but each on a single stem. They will not continue to thrive unless given Alpine conditions of superexcellent drainage and full sun.

The "wee crimson-tipped" ENGLISH DAISY is as great a pest in English lawns as the Dandelions are in ours, but it does not take kindly to America. It is best handled like Pansies and Forget-me-nots—by August planting and a light winter mulch. Then it will bring gaiety to your garden in early spring.

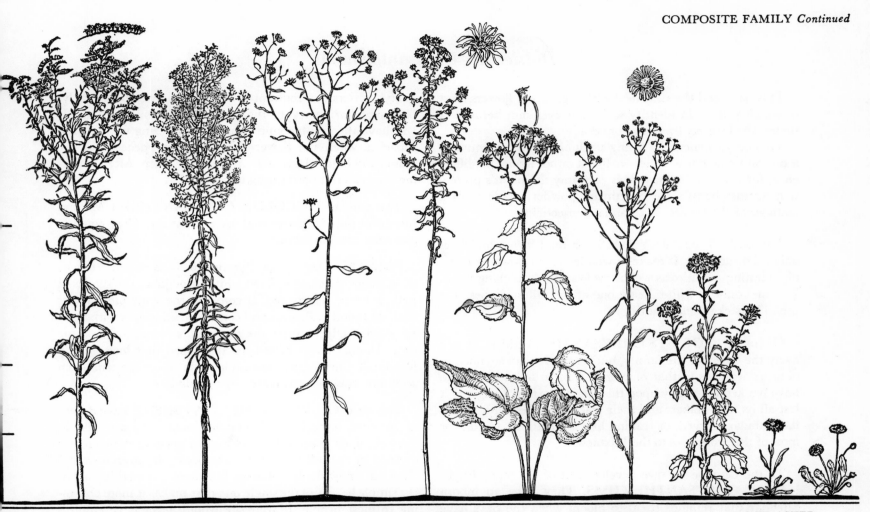

MARE'S-TAIL
Erigeron canadensis

NEW ENGLAND ASTER
Aster novae-angliae

DAISY FLEABANE
Erigeron annuus
(e-rij'-er-on)

ROCK ASTER
Aster alpinus
(as'-ter)

GOLDEN-ROD
Solidago
(sol-i-day'-goh)

BOLTONIA
Boltonia asteroides
(bohl-toh'-ni-ah)

LINDLEYS ASTER
Aster Lindleyanus

CHINA ASTER
Callistephus chinensis
(ka-lis'-te-fus)

ENGLISH DAISY
Bellis perennis
(bel'-is)

Daisies Are Chrysanthemums

This page and the next deal with a group of flowers most of which you could identify with your eyes shut because of their—shall we say fragrance or odor?

To most gardeners the strong smell of Chrysanthemums is a pleasant one, but whether we like it or not makes no difference, for it is here to stay. It is probably the plant's protection against bugs, since pyrethrum powder, made from a member of the family, is a standard insecticide.

The GIANT STARRY DAISY is mud-loving and likes only mild sunshine. It makes a wonderful cut flower because of its lasting qualities as well as its graceful branching habit. It comes only in white. Being one of the tallest daisies, it is useful in background plantings.

Of course FLORISTS CHRYSANTHEMUM is far and away the queen of the family, but that is due not so much to nature's work as to that of patient human hybridizers who have worked especially upon this tender variety. Long ago it lost all its seed-makers and their place was filled with petals, flat, tubular, curved, or trailing like tail feathers. Credit for most of this work goes to the Japanese.

To the Chinese we owe development of the many bright HARDY CHRYSANTHEMUMS. They have an inborn calendar that reminds them to bloom when the days have become of the proper shortness. This makes them open earliest in the North and later in the South. Clever florists have devices for shading their houses and thus forcing the early blooms that bring high prices.

Hybridizers are constantly working to develop the early-blooming hardier types that we want for our gardens. If you have the late-blooming kinds and freezing weather approaches when the flowers have not yet opened, pot the plants and enjoy them in your window garden. After flowering they can rest until spring in your cellar.

The annual TRICOLOR CHRYSANTHEMUMS are successful only in places that have moist air. They come in gay color combinations.

PAINTED DAISY, or Pyrethrum, is so called from its wide range of coloring, from white through all the shades of pink to deep, velvety red. It comes in the same pink shades that are found in Peonies and combines beautifully with them for garden effects, since the two plants bloom at the same time. Double forms have been developed that look exactly like small Chrysanthemums. These do not come true from seeds but must be propagated by root divisions.

The white OX-EYE and SHASTA DAISIES have dozens of varieties, some for each summer month. All are alike in insisting upon lime in the soil and in needing their crowns divided in the fall to prevent smothering by overcrowding. There are now double Shastas, but there is something about the simple beauty of the single one that makes it more charming to most people. Marguerite would never have embroidered the double ones on her gown. All are excellent for quantity use in the border. They blend or soften doubtful color combinations or accentuate distinctive plantings. The Daisies' resemblance to the sun gives the name "day's-eye."

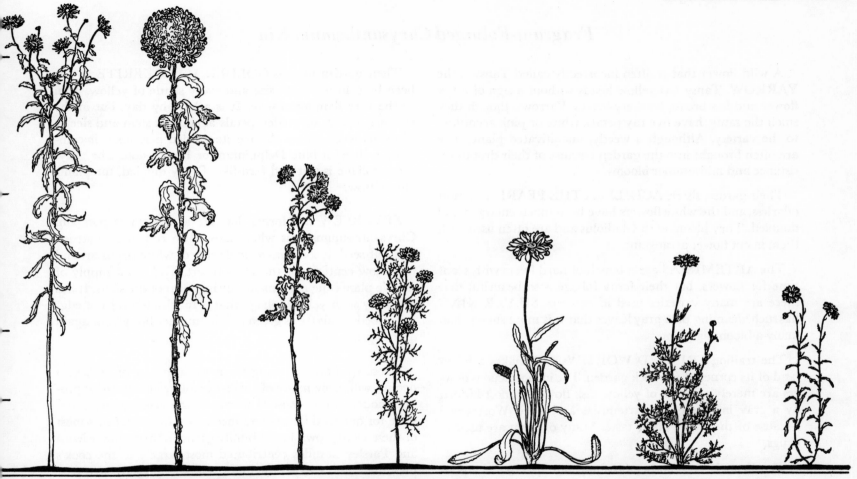

FLORISTS CHRYSANTHEMUM
Chrysanthemum morifolium

TRICOLOR CHRYSANTHEMUM
Chrysanthemum carinatum

PAINTED DAISY
Chrysanthemum coccineum

ANT STARRY DAISY
ysanthemum uliginosum

HARDY CHRYSANTHEMUM
Chrysanthemum
(kris-an'-the-mum)

SHASTA DAISY
Chrysanthemum maximum

OX-EYE DAISY
Chrysanthemum
Leucanthemum

Fragrant-Foliaged Chrysanthemum Kin

A wild flower that is often incorrectly called Tansy is the YARROW. Tansy has yellow heads without a sign of a ray flower and has broad, feathery leaves. Yarrows, though they smell the same, have five ray petals, white or pink according to the variety. Although a weedy, uncultivated plant, they are often brought into the garden because of their drouth resistance and midsummer blooms.

Their garden sister, ACHILLEA THE PEARL, is almost odorless, and the white flowers have been much enlarged and doubled. They bloom with Gladiolus and are often used with them in cut flower arrangements.

The ARTEMISIAS are a bunch of hard livers with scant time for flowers, but their ferny foliage is so beautiful that there are many varieties used in gardens. SILVER KING has such gleaming pale gray leaves that it is more showy than many a blooming plant.

The trailing FRINGED WORMWOOD makes a fairyland of its corner of the rock garden. The inconspicuous flowers are merely a bunch of yellow disk flowers almost hidden by a gray involucre. All Artemisias are called Wormwood because of their very bitter taste. Many of them are used as drugs.

The Fennels are another far-flung family. How the pungent odor of DOG FENNEL brings back the memory of old farmyards, where bare feet trailed through the white blossoms as one followed father about his evening work. And Dog Fennel tea! That was for stomach-aches.

Their garden form is GOLDEN MARGUERITE. It has been bred into a large size and every shade of yellow, even to the rare flaming orange. It is a lady by day, but in the evening it folds its golden petals against its stem and sleeps, as do its weed sisters. A favorite garden perennial, it combines well with blue Delphinium or Platycodon. The gray-green foliage is soft and fern-like. Easily divided, the plants also selfsow.

FEVERFEW has forms that are as double as pompom Chrysanthemums, but when allowed to run in the garden and self-seed, it soon has a single row of white petals around its yellow centers, for the seeds revert. To keep a supply of double plants one must make cuttings or root divisions. It has a variety with yellow foliage that is much used for the edging of beds. This turns green in late summer but yellow again in the spring.

Those who are following the new-old hobby of herb gardening will grow many of this fragrant group. In these prosaic modern times most of us run to the grocery and drugstore for our food flavors and medicines. In olden times most of these were grown in the family garden. Although the Mint and Parsley families contributed most largely to the cook's provisions, the Chrysanthemum relatives played their part too. Wormwoods were added to vinegar, leaves of Chrysanthemum were candied, and Tarragon gave a delicious flavor to salads. In the less popular field of bitters and medicine were classed Feverfew, Camomile, Wormwood, and Tansy.

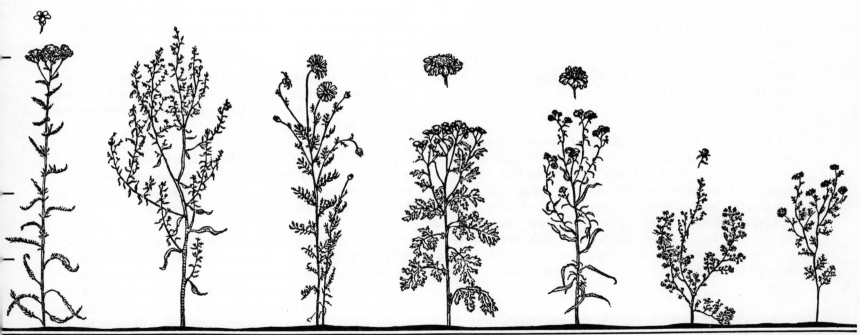

YARROW
Achillea Millefolium

SILVER KING
Artemisia albula
(ahr-tee-miz′-i-ah)

GOLDEN MARGUERITE
Anthemis tinctoria

FEVERFEW
Chrysanthemum Parthenium

THE PEARL
Achillea Ptarmica
(ak-i-lee′-ah)

FRINGED WORMWOOD
Artemisia frigida

DOG FENNEL
Anthemis Cotula
(an′-the-mis)

For Those Who Like Yellow

The Composite flowers that combine for us the rich shades of yellow, orange, and maroon are mostly in this group and are mostly natives of Mexico. No wonder the people of that country love to wear gay clothes, since so many of their flowers set them the example.

MARIGOLDS are the spendthrifts among annuals, pouring a wealth of gold, copper, and brass into our autumn gardens. We may have it in large coin or small, and they ask in return not even so much as our best garden soil. If we do not like the rank scent of their foliage, we may select the new odorless varieties.

SNEEZEWEEDS repeat the same autumn colors on tall background perennials. There are low ones and tall ones, yellow ones and deep red ones. Some even look like small copies of Blanket-flower, with assorted colors and notched ray flowers. Most of them bloom at the end of summer when flowering perennials are scarce. The name Sneezeweed is hardly fair, because they are not especially provocative of hay fever. A more gracious name used by some is Helensflower. They are easily grown from seed, divisions, or cuttings.

Perennial BLANKET-FLOWERS will endure the hottest locations and seem to enjoy hard soil. But they make larger flowers under more favorable conditions. Their name is suggested by the zigzag way in which the stripes of color are set in its bloom after the manner of those in Navajo Indian blankets. If you prefer plain colors, you can purchase varieties that are all yellow or all rich red.

Annual Blanket-flower forms its bloom heads entirely of trumpet-shaped disk flowers. Their value as cut flowers is not fully appreciated or they would be found in more gardens. They will last a week in a vase, even in the hottest weather, and their coloring of yellow and maroon is one that fits into almost any living room or library background.

LEOPARDS BANE is not closely related to this group and demands a cool situation with moist, rich soil. It sends up its yellow "Daisies" in April when such flowers are rare and rests in the summer.

POT MARIGOLD, or Calendula, is so named because it is willing to bloom throughout the calendar, outdoors until a heavy freeze and as a greenhouse flower the rest of the year. It is a favorite annual easily grown from seed.

Senecio is the family name for the simple native yellow GROUNDSEL of our spring woods. It is also the name of the highly perfected pot plants CINERARIAS, which are offered by florists each spring in a bewildering array of purples, magentas, and pinks. All winter they have been growing in a cool, moist greenhouse, and they will probably not last very long in your hot living room. But even though you succeed in keeping them only a few weeks, they are well worth the price. They are annuals and die when their crop of buds have all opened.

AZTEC MARIGOLD
Tagetes erecta
(tah-jee'-teez)

LEOPARDS BANE
Doronicum
(doh-ron'-i-kum)

POT MARIGOLD
Calendula
(kah-len'-deu-lah)

CINERARIA
Senecio cruentus
(se-nee'-shi-oh)

SNEEZEWEED
Helenium
(he-lee'-ni-um)

BLANKET FLOWER
Gaillardia
(gay-lahr'-di-ah)

GROUNDSEL
Senecio plattensis

Cone-flowers

All except one of the Composites on this page belong to the Cone-flower group, so we'll dispose of that odd one, SUNFLOWER HELIOPSIS, first. For some obscure botanical reason it is not a true Sunflower, though the "helio" part of its name means "sun." The true Sunflower, *Helianthus,* was too large for the space on this page, and anyway we are sure that you know how it looks. But did you know that the crook in its neck was not from the weight of the head but done to make seed-scattering easier? And did you know that there is no truth in the saying that it follows the sun with its face all day? Watch and see for yourself. The Sunflower Heliopsis, a native, blooms in the late summer, usually in sunny, moist lowlands.

The other flowers are Cone-flowers, and since the cones are brown, they are commonly called Black-eyed Susans. This name is often given to *Thunbergia alata.*

GOLDEN-GLOW, a stand-by bloomer for August gardens, is very double, but you will find a single-flowered native variety that shows the cone. It grows so easily in difficult places that a bunch of it should be placed in every dark corner of the shrubbery. Tiger Lilies, which bloom at the same time, combine with it effectively. It spreads comfortably, so that you may have the pleasure of sharing it with others. The single-flower type is interesting for a wild garden, especially if the area is moist.

The most graceful wildling of this group is called simply CONE-FLOWER. It has long, floating, yellow ray flowers and swaying stems. Mingled with lavender Horse Balm and Gayfeather, it makes a lovely roadside picture. You may also use it for background in your sunny border. It is considered a weed by farmers in some sections.

BROWN-EYED SUSAN, *Rudbeckia triloba,* gets its scientific name from the three lobes of its leaves. It is a biennial, but once with you it always stays, and each plant presents you with a mound of bloom that covers a square yard of space. It is one of those plants of which you always have a few more than you want but have not the heart to destroy. It blooms as well in shade as in sun and keeps well as a cut flower.

BLACK-EYED SUSAN is named *Rudbeckia hirta* (hairy) because it is so bristly that one can scarcely touch it. But it has a heart of gold and the color to match. It comes straight from the prairie to brighten dull perennial borders in July. You'll pick many a gay bouquet. The plant is biennial and selfsows, which is a welcome trait in our gardens but not in the farmer's fields.

The PURPLE CONE-FLOWER is not purple but lavender-pink as to ray flowers and has stiff brown points around its disk flowers. It is found in the most arid situations, especially liking to clamber over clay cuts along roadsides. Each bloom is solitary on its stem. Improved varieties are appearing in catalogues. You'll like its sturdy beauty in your garden.

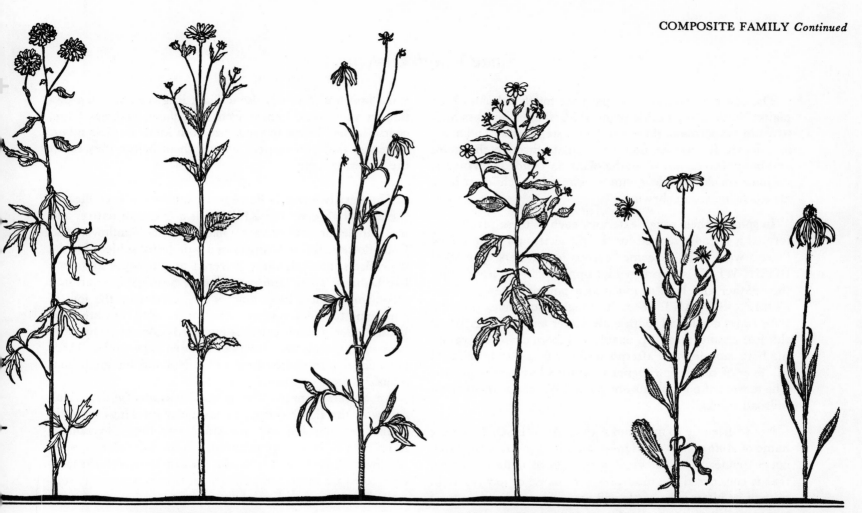

GOLDEN-GLOW
Rudbeckia laciniata

SUNFLOWER HELIOPSIS
Heliopsis helianthoides
(hee-li-op′-sis)

CONE-FLOWER
Lepachys pinnata
(lep′-ah-kis)

BROWN-EYED SUSAN
Rudbeckia triloba

BLACK-EYED SUSAN
Rudbeckia hirta
(rud-bek′-i-ah)

PURPLE CONE-FLOWER
Echinacea purpurea
(ek-i-nay′-she-ah)

Some Tough Customers

The first two plants on this page are tough old pals of the plains. While many prairie plants thicken their juices to milk to avoid evaporation, these weeds go a step farther and make it resinous. It must be fluid to circulate through the stems and broad leaves, but when the plant is wounded and bleeds, its juice quickly hardens into a gum, which children have always delighted in chewing.

In spite of their rough exteriors, each of these plants performed a friendly service for the pioneers, and their yellow flowers were often welcome beacons to travelers. The CUP ROSIN-WEED so arranges its upper pairs of leaves that they gather and hold as much as a pint of water. And the COMPASS PLANT keeps its tough, flat leaves pointing their edges north and south both winter and summer. While this leaf arrangement is probably an inborn device for catching both morning and afternoon sun, it is said to have saved the lives of many bewildered wayfarers lost on the prairie. The flowers of both plants are yellow. Watch for them along railroad tracks.

Not so friendly to mankind is the RAGWEED. Its family name of *Ambrosia* is a sad misnomer, for the calyx cups spill not a divine drink but great quantities of irritating pollen that is considered the most prevalent cause of hay fever. In spite of its bitter taste cattle will eat it when other pasture is scarce, and it gives an offensive taste to the milk. The name Ragweed probably comes from the tattered effect of its limp leaves. Fortunately their texture makes them easily susceptible to destruction by chemicals, so the fight against them

is not hopeless. There is also a Giant Ragweed, which grows tall, as you would expect from the name, and has large, coarse leaves. Learn to recognize both kinds in their infant stages, so that you can cut or pull them before they reach the flowering stage.

The next two sturdy flowers are among the friendliest of the annual garden. The ZINNIA is a Mexican native, and in its single form we can see a likeness to the Sunflowers and Cone-flowers. But it has proven a wonderful subject for the hybridizers, and the large-flowered double types are more like Dahlias. Their large seeds, quick germination, and sure bloom make them ideal flowers for introducing the joys of gardening to children or other beginners. And they are inexpensive. For a dime you can buy seeds enough to bring to your yard the glorious colors of a dozen sunset skies. There are midget forms to be used as borders and for small bouquets.

An especially pretty one is the Mexican Zinnia, which comes in the rich colorings and angular markings found in Indian art. The Fantasy type (tall) resembles Chrysanthemum both in its shaggy petals and in the soft coloring of its blossoms. Unfortunately the ones bred up to furnish the largest blooms are subject to mildew, but that may be easily controlled by dusting with sulphur.

For your rock garden be sure to use CREEPING-ZINNIA, a bright-flowered, annual, yellow trailer. It isn't a true Zinnia but certainly looks like one.

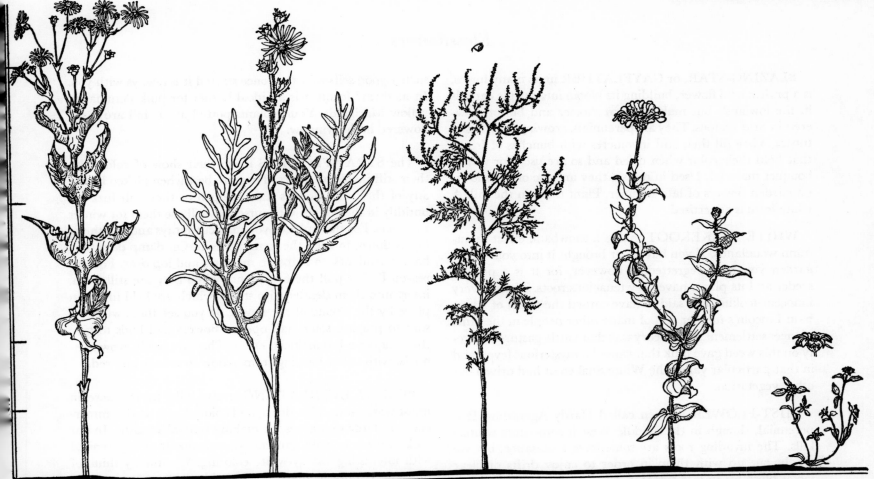

COMPASS PLANT
Silphium laciniatum

ZINNIA
Zinnia
(zin'-i-ah)

RAGWEED
Ambrosia artemisiifolia
(am-bro'-zee-ah)

CREEPING-ZINNIA
Sanvitalia procumbens
(san-vi-tay'-li-ah)

CUP ROSIN-WEED
Silphium perfoliatum
(sil'-fi-um)

Flossflowers

BLAZING-STAR, or GAYFEATHER in its many forms, is a prairie wild flower, building its bloom into purple cattails in the lowlands but making them shorter and button-flowered in arid regions. They are perennials, growing from fleshy tubers. They fill their stiff involucres with bunches of fringe that hold their color when dried and so are used for winter bouquet material. Used in masses they are one of the showiest garden flowers of late summer. Plant them in the fall. A white form is advertised.

WHITE SNAKEROOT makes a snowbank effect in autumn woodlands. If you have ever brought it into your shade garden you have regretted it, however, for it is a profuse seeder and its plants have very tenacious roots. Though very innocent-looking it is said to have caused the death of Abraham Lincoln's mother and of many other people in the same pioneer settlement. The theory was that cattle pastured largely on this weed gave milk that caused a mysterious fever, and in that particular valley the White Snakeroot had driven out other vegetation.

MIST-FLOWER is often called Hardy Ageratum. It is perennial, though in the Middle West it sometimes winterkills. The invading roots are sometimes a nuisance, but we gladly put up with them in order to enjoy drifts of clear violet blossoms in late summer, when most of the garden is drowsing. It is excellent with tall or dwarf pink Zinnias or lemon-yellow Marigolds.

The annual lavender Ageratum, or FLOSSFLOWER, is such a good selfsower that once started it is always with you. In its dwarf forms it is an ideal border for pink Petunias or yellow Marigolds. Young plants potted in the fall are easily flowered in the window.

The STRAWFLOWERS make their show of color with their stiff involucre scales. They are best when picked before any of their disk flowers start to open or they will fuzz out untidily in the winter. Of course you will use them for winter bouquets. For this purpose you may cut sprays and dry them, heads down, to keep the stems straight. On damp days they have a tendency to reabsorb moisture and lop over. For this reason florists pull the heads and, while they are still fresh, insert into them slender wire stems, which are held firmly in place by the drying of the flower. If you see these wires, be sure to prepare some half-opened flowers and buds to give the bouquet a less artificial effect. They are easily grown annuals, with colors varying from yellow to orange and red.

PEARLY EVERLASTING grows wild by the acre in moist wastelands. Cut, dried, and colored, it is used commercially in large quantities for making funeral wreaths. In our rock gardens or wild gardens we welcome it as a perennial with interesting woolly-white coloring. We usually think of the flowers only in mass, but individual blossoms resemble miniature Water-lilies.

PUSSY'S TOES is a tiny native flower with silvery foliage more attractive than its flowers.

BUTTON GAYFEATHER
Liatris squarrosa

MIST-FLOWER
Eupatorium coelestinum

STRAWFLOWER
Helichrysum
(hel-i-kry′-sum)

PUSSY'S TOES
Antennaria
(an-te-nay′-ri-ah)

BLAZING-STAR
Liatris scariosa
(ly-ay′-tris)

WHITE SNAKEROOT
Eupatorium urticaefolium
(eu-pah-toh′-ri-um)

FLOSSFLOWER
Ageratum
(a-jer′-ah-tum)

PEARLY EVERLASTING
Anaphalis margaritacea
(ah-naf′-al-is)

Lettuce and Other Paintbrush Flowers

Lettuce is the type plant for this page. Its name *Lactuca* refers to the milky juice, which is a group characteristic. Note the soft, bulky involucres, with points sometimes extending beyond the petals. The seeds are equipped with silk parachutes for flying on the wind.

This is a great salad family, furnishing not only the Lettuce but the Endive Chicory, which is especially popular in French markets. The tough leaves of the WILD LETTUCE taste bitter to us, but rabbits choose it above all other weeds. Even our own garden Lettuce will turn bitter as it matures and prepares to send up its flower stalk. That's why one should try to have a succession of plantings. As warmer weather approaches, the plants mature more rapidly.

The strap-petaled flowers of CHICORY are a clear, beautiful blue, but like those of the rest of this group they remain open only a few hours a day. Though we find the plant as a roadside weed, it is also cultivated in vegetable gardens. The leaves of seedlings are used as greens, and those of older plants are blanched for use in salads. The root too serves a practical purpose, being roasted and used as a substitute for coffee.

The other vegetable offering is SALSIFY, whose thick fleshy roots are cut into sections and used to make mock-oyster soup. Its purple, strap-leaved flowers are beautiful enough for the flower border, and it has an even more picturesque balloon for its seeds than has the Dandelion. The

Wild Salsify has yellow blooms, and its shaggy seed heads give it the name of Goat's Beard.

What shall we say about DANDELIONS? Perhaps that we might as well learn to admire their beauty, for they are absolutely indifferent to our opposition and proceed to annex for their own use any lawns into which their seeds float and fasten themselves by their barbed teeth. They protect themselves in many ways. Their juice is so bitter that they are avoided by grazing animals. They save their flower heads from the mower by keeping the stems very short on the lawn, but in tall grass they stretch up to catch the sun. Every flower in the head bears a banner and at its base grows the seed, which will take root and before fall establish a strong rosette, budded and all ready to blossom on the first sunny day of spring. The young leaves make excellent salad greens or pot herbs, and the roots are used in medicine.

There are several wild plants with small flowers that seem to copy the Dandelion. One of them is MOUNTAIN-DANDELION, also with yellow flowers. Since it does not become weedy, it is sometimes used in the rock garden.

HAWKWEED with its tawny orange paintbrush flowers and prickly leaves is a perennial that always attracts attention. Since it has become a pest in Eastern meadows, it should be used with caution and its seeds removed before they can take to their wings. It often grows much taller than the one we show in our illustration.

CHICORY
Cichorium Intybus
(si-koh'-ri-um)

MOUNTAIN-DANDELION
Krigia
(kri'-jah)

HAWKWEED
Hieracium
(hy-er-ay'-shi-um)

WILD LETTUCE
Lactuca canadensis
(lak-teu'-kah)

SALSIFY
Tragopogon porrifolius
(trag-oh-poh'-gon)

DANDELION
Taraxacum
(tah-rak'-sah-kum)

Index

129